Ligand
Substitution
Processes

FRONTIERS IN CHEMISTRY

Ronald Breslow and Martin Karplus, Editors
Columbia University

Ligand Substitution Processes

COOPER H. LANGFORD, *Amherst College*

HARRY B. GRAY, *Columbia University*

1966

W. A. BENJAMIN, INC.

ADVANCED BOOK PROGRAM

READING, MASSACHUSETTS

LONDON • AMSTERDAM • DON MILLS, ONTARIO • SYDNEY • TOKYO

LIGAND SUBSTITUTION PROCESSES

First printing, 1966
Second printing, with corrections, 1974

International Standard Book Number 0-8053-5822-0
Library of Congress Catalog Card Number 66-12702

ISBN 0-8053-5822-0
ABCDEFGHIJ-CO-7987654

Preface

The subject of the mechanistic study of ligand substitution reactions is currently undergoing an exciting growth. New fast-reaction techniques have removed the upper limit on rates that can be measured, and extension to less familiar central metal atoms has begun in earnest. This might seem the wrong moment for review of the field. As yet, definitive treatment is possible only for those complexes involving monodentate ligands with cobalt(III) and platinum(II). But, because information is so extensive for these systems, it is clear that they are functioning as models from which concepts and experiments are generated for application over the fast-growing range of the subject. We believe that this is an important moment to reopen debate on fundamentals so that concepts will be most felicitously formulated to aid growth of understanding. This monograph is centrally concerned with three aspects of those fundamentals.

We have attempted to develop an approach to classification of ligand substitution reactions that is adapted to what seem to have emerged as the characteristic features of these reactions and is susceptible to operational tests. (We do recognize that any such scheme of ideas is necessarily obsolescent once it is formulated since new experiments will certainly follow immediately.) We have tried to evaluate the basis for making generalizations about ligand substitution processes and to formulate tests to show whether new reactions fall within familiar patterns. Finally, we have sought to base the models of ligand substitution processes in the language of molecular-orbital theory. We believe that MO theory is most useful, because it may be used to correlate rate data on complexes with the extensive information available from spectral and magnetic studies, yet differs from crystal-field theory in providing a natural place for consideration of the *bonding* electrons, which must be a principal determinant of reaction processes.

To keep this essay within bounds, we assume familiarity with the elements of experimental kinetics, transition-state theory, and the simple molecular-orbital theory of complexes. Introductory physical chemistry,

some familiarity with the study of reaction mechanisms, and mastery of
one of the qualitative treatments of MO theory as applied to transition-
metal complexes should provide sufficient background. Thus, we hope
that this book will be useful to students, relatively early in their careers,
who wish to explore this field.

Our debts to very many workers will be obvious throughout. We
want to record here our special personal debt to Professors Ralph G.
Pearson and Fred Basolo and to Dr. Martin Tobe. We particularly
thank Professor George S. Hammond for his interest and enthusiasm in
this project. Professor Hammond carefully read and criticized the
entire manuscript in the final drafts. We received many other valuable
criticisms at various stages of this project from Professors R. D. Archer,
F. Basolo, J. O. Edwards, J. Finholt, P. Haake, J. Halpern, A. Kropf,
R. G. Pearson, S. I. Shupack, M. S. Silver, and C. Walling, and Dr. U.
Belluco and Dr. L. Cattalini. We very much appreciate their help and
probably should have followed their suggestions more closely. We
warmly acknowledge expert assistance from Mrs. Madeline deFriesse,
Miss Jan Denby, and Mrs. Diane Celeste in preparation of the manuscript.

COOPER H. LANGFORD
HARRY B. GRAY

Amherst, Massachusetts
New York, New York
October 1965

Contents

chapter one

Introduction

Ligand substitution reactions of coordination compounds have been studied as intensively as any class of inorganic reactions. These are the reactions for which the generalized equation (1-1) may be written. In Eq. (1-1), M is a metal atom and X and Y are any two ligands. (One of

$$MX_n + Y = MX_{n-1}Y + X \qquad (1\text{-}1)$$

the ligands involved is often also the solvent species.) The general form encompasses both some very fast and some quite slow reactions as well as coordination compounds of both transition and nontransition metals. The bulk of the experimental work, however, is concerned with those complexes of transition metals which are nonlabile. That is, the majority of the effort to date has been devoted to the study of reactions slow enough to be accessible to classical kinetic techniques. Detailed information has appeared for reactions involving the d^6 metal system Co(III), the d^8 metal system Pt(II), and to a lesser extent the d^3 system Cr(III). Some important information is now appearing concerning Rh(III), Au(III), and Pd(II). We shall adopt the point of view that these better understood systems are paradigmatic of, at least, the methods and concepts appropriate to the study of ligand substitutions in general. A later section (Section 3-16) undertakes a preliminary test of the applicability of the concepts derived from the "classical" systems to reactions of labile complexes, using the interesting data derived from the new fast-reaction methods, but the bulk of the discussion is devoted to well-known reactions of the type given in Eqs. (1-2) and (1-3). These two examples also

$$Co(NH_3)_5Cl^{2+} + H_2O \rightleftharpoons Co(NH_3)_5OH_2^{3+} + Cl^- \qquad (1\text{-}2)$$

$$Pt(NH_3)_3Cl^+ + I^- \rightleftharpoons Pt(NH_3)_3I^+ + Cl^- \qquad (1\text{-}3)$$

represent the two structural types for which extensive data are available, the approximately octahedral six-coordinate complexes, and the approximately square-planar four-coordinate complexes.

Most mechanistic analysis is based on the study of reaction-rate processes, and it is natural to divide the task into two distinct phases. The first is discovery of the sequence of elementary steps by which a complicated over-all reaction is accomplished, and the second is to understand the magnitudes of the rate constants for the individual steps in terms of the rearrangements of atoms and bonds (electrons) taking place. We shall designate the elaboration of the reaction in terms of elementary steps the study of the *stoichiometric* mechanism, and the analysis of the individual steps the study of *intimate* mechanism. The classification of ligand substitution reactions has been based principally on differences of stoichiometric mechanism. Conceptually, this has seemed straightforward. It is usually easy to write down plausible reaction schemes with definite steps and intermediates. But, the question of stoichiometric mechanism is often the hardest to resolve experimentally. Partly, this results from conceptual confusions. To construct the most useful language for discussion of ligand substitution, we must explore the relation of theories of reaction-rate processes to the *experimentally* meaningful definition of elementary reaction step for reactions in solution.

There are two theoretical models available for our discussion, the collision theory [1] and the transition-state theory.[2] Most discussions of mechanisms of reactions in solution are based on the vocabulary and concepts of the transition-state theory. In this theory, it is possible to refine the concept of elementary step almost indefinitely. Clearly, any local minimum in a potential surface may be regarded as an intermediate species requiring treatment of the reaction as multistep. But, it is not clear that all such minima are accessible to experiment.

Consider, as an example, a situation that is actually favorable for experimental intermediate detection, the solvolysis of a halo-complex RX, according to Eq. (1-4). S denotes a solvent molecule that may function

$$RX + S = RS^+ + X^- \qquad (1-4)$$

as a ligand. Assume that the transition state for this substitution is reached by a considerable degree of rupture of the bond to the leaving X group. There are two possibilities: The substitution may proceed smoothly in a concerted single step, or an intermediate of reduced coordination number (R^+) may be formed prior to the entry of the solvent molecule. These two paths are illustrated on a conventional potential versus reaction coordinate diagram of transition-state theory in Figure 1-1. Curve (a) illustrates the one-step path and curve (b) the two-step path. Conceptually, the distinction is plain. How is it to be made experimentally?

One approach would be through "kinetic" experiments. The existence of unstable intermediates that never accumulate enough for direct observation may modify rate laws in anticipatable ways because an intermediate may react *selectively*. Introduction of free X^- ion into the solution might lead to a reduction in the observed solvolysis rate. This would serve as evidence for the intermediate, if it could be interpreted as indication of diversion of the intermediate from solvolysis back to the initial complex. (Some care must be taken to exclude other possible effects of X^-.) Simi-

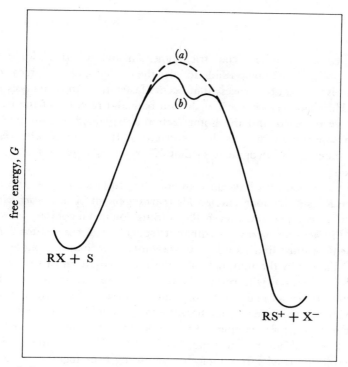

Figure 1-1   *Free energy vs. reaction progress diagram for solvolysis of a halo-complex RX.   Curve (a) represents the concerted process.   Curve (b) includes an intermediate of reduced coordination number.*

larly, other competitors for the intermediate might lead to a change in the product distribution without affecting the rate of disappearance of the initial complex. A still more subtle way to observe selective reactivity of an intermediate follows the ideas of Winstein et al.[3] Consider the effects of introducing the noncoordinating anion perchlorate to the reaction system in a solvent that represses ionic dissociation. If the intermediate is formed in this solvent, it may remain for some time as an ion pair, from which the leaving group will be able to re-enter the complex to give no over-all reaction. Addition of excess perchlorate can lead to replacement of the leaving group in the ion pair by perchlorate, which preserves the intermediate for solvolysis [Eq. (1-5)]. The net result is a special acceleration of solvolysis on the addition of perchlorate that is not produced by other salts. Finally, in the event that RX has

$$RX \rightleftharpoons R^+ \cdots X^- \overset{ClO_4^-}{\rightleftharpoons} R^+ \cdots ClO_4^- + X^- \qquad (1\text{-}5)$$

$$\downarrow S$$

$$RS^+$$

properties of optical or geometric isomerism and R^+ is a highly symmetric species, it may be possible to infer the existence of the intermediate from an isomerization process that occurs faster than the solvolysis reaction. Here again, formation of the ion pair and re-entry of the leaving group are involved, but the isomerization is explained by assuming that the ion pair survives at least long enough for R^+ to rotate with respect to its immediate environment so that X^- re-entry may be from a new direction.

All the above tests have in common the requirement that the intermediate R^+ survive long enough for rearrangement of its *contact solvation shell*. (The contact solvation shell of a transition metal complex is usually called the *outer* or *second* coordination sphere.) A competitor for the intermediate must find its way into the outer coordination sphere of the intermediate. In the minimal case, the intermediate must survive long enough for rotations with respect to its outer coordination sphere. From the point of view of collision theory, the requirement for detection of an intermediate is that the intermediate last long enough for exchanges of collision partners before reacting. In solution, the solvent-cage effect[4] operates to keep collision partners together for 10 to 10^2 successive collisions. This recollision results from molecules bouncing back together from collisions with surrounding solvent molecules and is predicted from almost any model of the liquid state, whether it be a quasi-lattice or disordered liquid model. The succession of connected collisions is called an *en-*

counter, and an intermediate cannot be detected by the above "kinetic" tests if it can react within a single encounter.   There must be a significant activation energy for reaction of the intermediate if it is to be detected. On a time scale, it must survive longer than a minimum near 10^{-10} sec. This figure refers to the most favorable cases for intermediate detection.

For short-lived intermediates, it would be necessary to find tests that did not involve modification of the rate law (tests not involving modification of the kinetic stoichiometry—which will be called *nonkinetic* in this chapter).   Some attempts have been made to judge the timing of bond breaking and bond formation in substitutions from analysis of reaction energetics.   This involves comparison of the rates of closely related reactions.[5]   Essentially, these are attempts to convert data on the energy difference between the ground state and the transition state into information about the shape of the potential function for the reaction.   Such attempts have been criticized cogently by Hammond,[6] with the aid of one postulate:

> If two states (as, for example, a transition state and an unstable intermediate) occur consecutively during a reaction process and have nearly the same energy content, their interconversion will require only a small reorganization of molecular structures.

Consider again the substitution reactions of RX, assuming that R^+ may be a short-lived intermediate (that is, lie at a shallow minimum in the potential surface).   Suppose that the composition of the outer coordination sphere (encounter complex) is altered by varying concentrations in the solution so that there is an opportunity for a variety of species to compete with the solvent on an even basis, resulting in a variety of substitution products in the different cases.   If the *rate of RX consumption is not altered* in these experiments, it would be inferred that the entering group (S or one of the others) does not significantly affect the energy of the transition state, and it might be argued that the entering group did not participate in the transition state and that the *intermediate was formed*. This second conclusion is, at best, highly *uncertain*.   Hammond's postulate indicates that the structure of a short-lived intermediate must be close to the transition state for its conversion to product.   The entering group cannot play a large role in the transition state that must include it. Thus there is no real argument for excluding the entering group from the transition state of the over-all reaction simply because it does not play a large energetic role.

We infer that *the only intermediates in substitution reactions that have experimental significance are those detected by what we have called "kinetic" tests.*   Any substitution that takes place within an encounter (faster than the reorgani-zation of the outer coordination sphere) must be considered, operationally, a concerted process. It will not be experimentally possible to exclude any species involved in the encounter from participation in the transition state. Conversely, it is important to realize that concerted processes may have a wide variety of transition states. The term *concerted* tends to evoke the image of entering-group bond formation providing energetic assistance to leaving-group bond rupture. As indicated above, the participation of the entering group may be entirely "accidental." (When the initial complex is activated "dissociatively," it must react with the ligand that is in place, if it cannot fall to a reasonably stable intermediate state.) Per-haps the term "concerted" is not the most appropriate for all substitution reactions occurring in a single elementary step. We prefer the less evoca-tive term *interchange*, indicating that the reaction process is an exchange of ligands between the inner and outer coordination spheres.

The RX solvolysis example was chosen as a case that offers the greatest sensitivity in intermediate detection. In other circumstances, hypotheti-cal unstable intermediates of longer lifetimes may still remain undetect-able. Two cases are of particular importance in what follows. First, the lifetimes of species in the outer coordination sphere of a metal com-plex may be long when special interactions exist. For example, the outer sphere complex between $Mn^{2+}(aq)$ and SO_4^{2-} has a dissociation rate constant [7] of 3.5×10^7 sec^{-1} (not more than 50 times the rate con-stant for dissociation of the inner-sphere complex). Second, when an intermediate is formed by addition of a ligand to produce an intermediate of *increased* coordination number, there will be no possible tests based on the selective reactivity of the intermediate. This problem is discussed in Section 1-3.

The above discussion has focused on the idea that experiments con-nected with the rate law and stoichiometry of a reaction are essential to identification of intermediates, elaboration of elementary steps, and as-signment of stoichiometric mechanism. The experiments that explore the effects of structure variation, or variation of other parameters, on the rate constant are those that provide the best information available, within the context of transition-state theory, about intimate mechanism: namely, the role played by various groups in activation energetics. As Ham-mond [6] pointed out, the inability to distinguish between a transition state and a metastable intermediate is of small importance when it is recognized that the disability arises from the fact that the hypothetical intermediate is a good model of the transition state of the reaction. The only important point is to avoid confusing experiments that provide information on the intimate mechanism with those that provide information on the stoichio-metric mechanism.

1-2 CLASSIFICATION OF LIGAND SUBSTITUTION MECHANISMS

In establishing a descriptive language for a group of reactions, there is always some danger that a scheme set up before all the facts are in will function more as a straitjacket to thought than as a guide to the orderly asking and answering of questions. But if a systematic analysis is to be developed, some categories must be imposed. Hopefully, an open mind toward any scheme can be preserved.

The most natural division in mechanistic study is that between stoichiometric and intimate mechanism, and it is perhaps equally natural to attempt categorizing from each of these points of view separately. The classical categories of substitution mechanism introduced in organic chemistry by Hughes and Ingold [8] and later applied to ligand substitution processes were originally based on a feature of stoichiometric mechanism, the *molecularity* of the rate-determining step of the reaction. These have been the source of some difficulty, since they have not always seemed to focus on the most interesting issues in ligand substitution processes. To understand why this may occur, it is helpful to think again of a bimolecular reaction in solution from the collisional point of view. When two particles collide in solution, they are caught in a *solvent cage*. Conversely, energy transfer in a condensed phase is rapid, and it is not reasonable to expect a system to remain in a highly "activated" state long enough for several exchanges of collision partners. As a result, a case of more or less "accidental bimolecularity" arises. A ligand may come into contact with a complex which then receives sufficient energy to dissociate. The new ligand enters the complex without having made any significant contribution to activation. It simply occupied the appropriate place within the solvation shell. The current categorization of substitution mechanisms includes cases which seem bimolecular in the strict *stoichiometric* sense but which are thought to be related to unimolecular cases, because their *intimate mechanism* seems to behave like that of the unimolecular process. [9]

A reformulation is possible that distinguishes categories of stoichiometric mechanism from categories of intimate mechanism and provides a natural place for "cage" reactions. The first task is to anticipate the types of stoichiometric mechanism that will be important in ligand substitutions and to choose designations for these. Subsequently, the scheme may be extended to cover interesting differences in intimate mechanism.

Three possible *simple* pathways are "stoichiometrically" distinct: a *dissociative* path (**D**) in which the leaving ligand is lost in the first step, producing an intermediate of reduced coordination number; an *associative* (**A**) path in which the entering ligand adds in the first step, producing an intermediate of increased coordination number; and the concerted path called *interchange* (I) (vide supra), since the leaving group is moving from the inner to the outer coordination sphere and the entering group is moving from outer to inner. (An interchange may occur along a multistep path, since the formation and dissociation of an outer-sphere complex may often be easily separable steps of a reaction, but the defining characteristic of interchange is the absence of an intermediate in which the primary coordination number of the metal is modified.) The three paths are illustrated in Eqs. (1-6), (1-7), and (1-8). (MX_n · · · Y

$$MX_n \underset{+Y}{\overset{-X}{\rightleftharpoons}} MX_{n-1} \underset{-X}{\overset{+Y}{\rightleftharpoons}} MX_{n-1}Y \qquad (\mathbf{D} = \text{dissociative}) \qquad (1\text{-}6)$$

$$MX_n \underset{-Y}{\overset{+Y}{\rightleftharpoons}} MX_nY \underset{+X}{\overset{-X}{\rightleftharpoons}} MX_{n-1}Y \qquad (\mathbf{A} = \text{associative}) \qquad (1\text{-}7)$$

$$MX_n \cdot \cdot \cdot Y \rightarrow MX_{n-1}Y \cdot \cdot \cdot X \qquad (\mathbf{I} = \text{interchange}) \qquad (1\text{-}8)$$

represents an outer-sphere complex, for example, an ion pair such as $Co(NH_3)_6^{3+}$ · · · SO_4^{2-}.) In this scheme the nature of the intermediate is the crucial factor. We find three possibilities that would reduce to only two if molecularity were made central.

The most useful distinction to make in the classification of intimate mechanisms of substitution is probably to distinguish between those reactions whose activation energy is markedly affected by the *assistance* of the entering group and those reactions whose activation energy is determined by the requirements of *dissociation*. These will be called the *associative* and *dissociative* modes of activation, and the corresponding categories of intimate mechanism will be designated **a** and **d**. Clearly, they are to be recognized by the criterion of the effect of the entering group on the rates of a series of related substitutions. If the rate is sensitive to the nature of the entering group, the reactions are **a**. If it is not possible to establish a dependence of the rate on the nature of the entering group that is in excess of what may be regarded simply as the effects of the entering group on the environment (for example, solvent effects), the reaction is **d**. It will be easily seen that the **A** and **D** categories will be isomorphous with useful categories of intimate mechanism, but that it is desirable to further subdivide **I** processes.

Figures 1-2 and 1-3 show energy versus reaction coordinate profiles for **A** and **D** processes, respectively. In the **A** process, both leaving and entering groups are participants in the transition state, and a role for the entering group in determining the activation energy is expected to be a characteristic feature. In a **D** process, the entering group does not participate in the transition state for the formation of the intermediate.

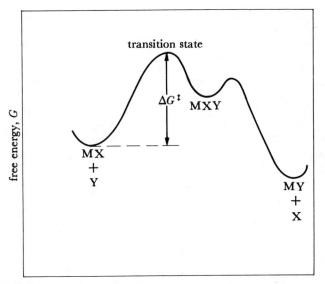

Figure 1-2   *Energy profile of an associative reaction. $\Delta G^{\ddagger}$ is the free energy of activation.*

Thus complete absence of an energetic role for the entering group may be considered the characteristic feature of the **D** process.

I reactions may have a variety of transition states, but two well-defined types will be those resembling the transition states of **A** and **D** reactions. The **A**-like transition in an **I** process will display substantial bonding to both the entering and leaving groups, and the entering group will play an important part in determining its energy.   Such a transition state on an **I** path will be indicated by adding the notation **a**.   The **D**-like transition state of **I** reactions is one with only weak bonding to both the entering and leaving groups (the bonding may be very weak indeed).   The entering group effect on rate will be small.   Such an **I** process will be denoted with an added **d**.

The **a-d** dichotomy appears to be the only subdivision of **I** processes that is necessary for a comprehensive discussion of ligand substitutions. There has been a persistent undercurrent of argument in the field over the extent to which it is possible to make generalizations about substitution mechanisms.   Some authors feel that broad similarities exist among the reaction mechanisms in a family of complexes.   Others have held that each reaction has a distinctive mechanism of its own.   There is truth in both views.   We believe that the two types of activation represent the

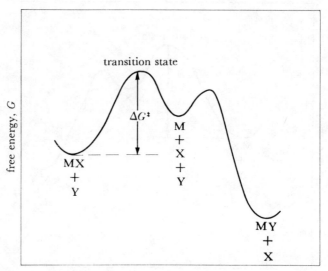

Figure 1-3   *Energy profile of a dissociative reaction.   Labels as in Figure 1-2.*

features about which generalizations can be made. The evidence in Chapters 2 and 3 suggests that each family of complexes undergoes substitution with a characteristic activation type (either **a** or **d**) but that there may well be differences of stoichiometric mechanism within a closely related family of complexes.

If the suggested classification of intimate mechanism is to be satisfactory, it must have significance with respect to other kinds of variations, in addition to the change of entering and leaving group. Some of the main types of experiments are steric modifications, modification of electronic characteristics of ligands attached to the reacting site, solvent modifications, and solvent and ligand kinetic-isotope effects. In fact, such studies have normally been analyzed in terms of their bearing on bond formation and bond rupture. Steric effects are a good example. It is argued that increase of steric crowding at a site will increase the activation energy for bond formation, but may reduce the activation energy for bond rupture as a result of relief of strain in the transition state.

Finally, it must be noted that intimate mechanisms are determined by reaction potential surfaces which may, in principle, be varied continuously. A division of intimate mechanisms into classes will remain somewhat arbitrary.

Table 1-1   *Classification of ligand substitution mechanisms*

	Stoichiometric mechanism		
Intimate mechanism	Intermediate of increased coordination number	Concerted process	Intermediate of reduced coordination number
Associative activation	**A**	$\mathbf{I_a}$	
Dissociative activation		$\mathbf{I_d}$	**D**

With three stoichiometric categories, one of which must be subdivided when intimate mechanisms are considered, a total of four mechanisms are sufficient for characterization of ligand substitutions. They are **A**, $\mathbf{I_a}$, $\mathbf{I_d}$, and **D**. Their characteristics are summarized in Table 1-1.

1-3 OPERATIONAL TESTS OF MECHANISM

The proposed classification scheme can be made operational (at least in principle). The distinction between assisted and unassisted activation has already been indicated. It depends on the idea that bonding is selective and that covalency in the transition state is characterized by the same feature that characterizes ground-state covalency, namely, a high sensitivity to the nature of the participating atoms. If the rates of a series of reactions which may be assumed to have related mechanisms show much smaller sensitivity to the nature of the entering group than to the nature of the leaving group, activation is classed as *dissociative*. This situation corresponds to an entering ligand effect small enough that it cannot be assigned unambiguously to covalency effects, if proper account is to be taken of the effects of ligand alteration on the environment of the reaction (for example, ionic strength). When rate changes with entering-group variation become comparable to the rate changes on variation of the leaving group, activation is characterized as associative.

The distinction between a dissociative (**D**) process and an interchange ($\mathbf{I_d}$) is made on kinetic grounds. The various possible tests were described in Section (1-1) in connection with the example of the **d** solvolysis of a halo-complex RX. The rate laws associated with these tests are considered in Chapter 3.

The distinction between the interchange, I_a, and associative, **A**, processes should be made on a basis similar to the I_d-**D** distinction. A mechanism will be called associative if it is possible to detect a two-step path involving increase of coordination number by kinetic or stereochemical techniques. Unfortunately, there is no analog of the competition experiments when all participants in the reaction are present in both steps of the two-step path. Moreover, the stereochemistry will normally be determined by the direction of initial attack. Thus we may detect an intermediate only if the intermediate is sufficiently stable to accumulate. The reaction shown in Figure 1-2 may be run in the direction such that the transition state lies after the intermediate. If the intermediate is sufficiently stable, the rate will not increase without limit as the entering-group concentration is raised. If the equilibrium leading to intermediate formation begins to become saturated, the rate will approach a limiting value. The rate law will fall toward first order. This observation is a necessary condition for an **A** reaction, but not sufficient!

Detection of an intermediate by its accumulation is a stringent test. We might easily imagine a significant intermediate in the sense of transition-state theory which is insufficiently stable to accumulate. (Some such intermediates are presumably detected in **D** processes.) This sort has been discussed in the context of aromatic substitution reactions. Criteria for intermediate detection have been advanced by Hughes et al.,[10] Melander,[11] and Bunnett and co-workers.[12] But these criteria have been criticized by Hammond.[6] We repeat his argument to show why detection of an intermediate of increased coordination number also *remains operationally uncertain* in the absence of the "kinetic" test.

In Figure 1-4 a minimum corresponding to a metastable intermediate is shown at S. The accounts of relative reactivity in aromatic substitution cited above have considered the transition state to be similar to the intermediate at S in which the carbon atom undergoing substitution has been converted to the tetrahedral configuration [see Eq. (1-9)]. If

$$(1-9)$$

such an intermediate is unstable, and has an energy of formation reasonably similar to the energy of activation, *it should be closely related to both the transition states R and T through which it is formed and destroyed by a* simple application of Hammond's postulate.

The criteria for detection of nonaccumulating intermediates in aromatic substitutions are all closely similar. Melander's discussion [11] of the use of a deuterium-isotope effect is a good specific case to consider. In aromatic nitration and bromination, Melander found that replacement of the hydrogen at the reaction site with tritium resulted in no kinetic-isotope effect. He argued that this indicated intermediate (1-9), since it suggested that the rate-determining step of the reaction did not involve breaking of the C—H bond. (Bunnett and Ingold et al. also argued similarly for the intermediate from an absence of a leaving-group effect on rate.) If the intermediate is unstable and its decomposition is highly

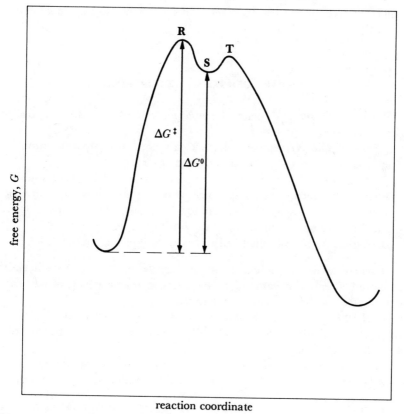

Figure 1-4   *Energy profile showing a metastable intermediate at S. $\Delta G^{\ddagger}$, the activation energy, determines the rate of the forward process.   Note that it is similar to ΔG°, the free energy of formation of the intermediate.*

exothermic, it follows from Hammond's postulate that only very small C—H bond stretching will be required to reach the transition state for decomposition of the intermediate (T in Figure 1-4). Thus there would be no more than a small kinetic-isotope effect on the step of the reaction that *does* involve breaking of the C—H bond. Absence of an isotope effect is not really inconsistent with either formation or decomposition of the intermediate as the rate-determining step of the reaction. Clearly, then, it is also consistent with a single-step process as well. [We should note that Olah and Kuhn later prepared[13] stable salts containing cations of the structure shown in (1-9).] Small leaving-group effects do not establish the sequence: bond formation preceding bond rupture. They do show that the transition state for the reaction involves a bond to the leaving group that has been minimally perturbed from its original ground state. As before, it is important to note that the proposed test reveals much of importance about the intimate mechanism, while leaving uncertainties about the stoichiometric mechanism.

1-4 SUMMARY OF MECHANISTIC CLASSIFICATIONS

There are three categories of *stoichiometric* mechanisms distinguished *operationally* by kinetic tests.

1. *Dissociative* (**D**): intermediate of reduced coordination number, which may be detected by its selective reactivity.

2. *Associative* (**A**): intermediate of increased coordination number, which may be detected by departure of the rate expression from strict second-order kinetics when the reaction is followed in the direction for which the transition state lies after the intermediate.

3. *Interchange* (**I**): no kinetically detectable intermediates.

There are two major categories of *intimate* mechanism that may be distinguished *operationally* if it can be assumed that a group of reactions with related mechanism can be identified.

1. *Associative activation* (**a**): the reaction rate is approximately as sensitive (or more sensitive) to variation of the entering group as to variation of the leaving group.

2. *Dissociative activation* (**d**): the reaction rate is much more sensitive to variation of the leaving group than to variation of the entering group.

D mechanisms must be dissociative. **A** mechanisms must be associative. Therefore, we adopt the following as the simplest combined notations designating both *stoichiometric* and *intimate* mechanism: **A**, **I$_a$**, **I$_d$**, **D**.

1-5 CORRELATION OF CLASSIFICATION SCHEMES

The present mechanistic designations may be correlated with those based on the Hughes-Ingold scheme. The **A** mechanism of ligand substitution would be labeled S_N2 or, in the refined version of Basolo and Pearson,[9] S_N2 lim. It is a process in which the rate-determining step is bimolecular. The **D** mechanism has a unimolecular rate-determining step and corresponds to the S_N1 lim process. The $\mathbf{I_a}$ case corresponds to the S_N2 (not limiting) mechanism.

The case that responds to tests of intimate mechanism as if dissociation of the leaving group were the important aspect of activation, but for which evidence for an intermediate of reduced coordination number is not forthcoming, has always been the ambiguous case in the Hughes-Ingold scheme. It is difficult to decide whether the failure to establish unimolecularity should be allowed to override the obvious similarities in behavior to the S_N1 lim process. Various attitudes have been adopted by various authors, and the processes here designated $\mathbf{I_d}$ have sometimes been called S_N1 and sometimes S_N2, usually with the recognition that they are borderline. (The introduction of the $\mathbf{I_d}$ notation is meant not only to avoid the ambiguity with respect to molecularity but also to *raise the question of possible "accidental bimolecularity"* in the sense described earlier.)

In the Hughes-Ingold scheme the abbreviation S_N signifies "substitution-nucleophilic," emphasizing the point that the metal complex undergoing substitution is a center not saturated with respect to electrons and that the ligand is an electron donor "seeking" a positive center in reaction. Nucleophile is often used as the kinetic term corresponding to the equilibrium concept of Lewis base.[14] The opposite kind of reagent is an electrophilic reagent, that is, one that attacks an electron-rich center. The distinction between electrophilic and nucleophilic attack at carbon centers is probably quite clear-cut. However, the transition metals with partly filled d shells often have available electrons at the reaction site. It is clear that the equilibrium properties of metal-ligand bonds are often strongly influenced by "back-donation" of electrons from the metal to the ligand. It is reasonable to assume that there is a kinetic analog of this phenomenon, and the term [15] "biphilic" has been introduced for reagents that both donate electrons to, and receive electrons from, the metal atom under attack. Although it is no doubt true that the vast majority of reactions in which one ligand replaces another are conveniently called nucleophilic substitutions, the exceptions are interesting. **The assumption of nucleophilicity is not built into our nomenclature.**

1-6 PROSPECTUS

The history of investigations of the reactions of families of complexes exhibits a common pattern. First, it is usually found that a particular rate law is fairly general. Second, the rate constants for the members of the family are compared to see if the effects of structure variation can be interpreted. This stage leads to more elaborate structure-variation studies and in some cases to deeper examination of the rate laws. This general history encourages interpretation to develop along certain lines. The rate laws do not usually settle the issue of stoichiometric mechanism, although they limit the possibilities. The structure-variation studies usually point to a pattern in the intimate mechanism. Unambiguous decisions on the final questions of stoichiometric mechanism are rare.

The next two chapters discuss the hypothesis that the two major structural types of transition metal complexes which have been studied extensively (octahedral and square-planar) each display a characteristic intimate mechanism. This may be shown to follow from theoretical expectations based on electronic and steric considerations. However, it is not maintained that the community of intimate mechanism in each type is close enough to exclude a crossover of a stoichiometric mechanism boundary. Evidence for such crossovers exists, but *this question remains very much in need of study.*

REFERENCES

1. E. A. Moelwyn-Hughes, *The Kinetics of Reactions in Solution*, 2nd ed., Oxford University Press, London, 1947.
2. S. Glasstone, K. S. Laidler, and H. Eyring, *The Theory of Rate Processes*, McGraw-Hill, New York, 1941.
3. S. Winstein, E. Clippinger, A. H. Fainberg, R. Heck, and G. C. Robinson, *J. Am. Chem. Soc.*, **78,** 328 (1956); S. Winstein and E. Clippinger, *J. Am. Chem. Soc.*, **78,** 2784 (1956); S. Winstein and A. H. Fainberg, *J. Am. Chem. Soc.*, **80,** 459 (1958); and earlier papers referred to therein.
4. S. Benson, *Foundations of Chemical Kinetics*, McGraw-Hill, New York, 1960, p. 543ff.
5. A recent discussion from this viewpoint appears in M. W. Hughes and M. L. Tobe, *J. Chem. Soc.*, **1965,** 1204.
6. G. S. Hammond, *J. Am. Chem. Soc.*, **77,** 334 (1955).
7. G. Atkinson, Abstr. Papers, 149th National Meeting, American Chemical Society, Detroit, April 4–9, 1965.
8. See C. K. Ingold, *Structure and Mechanism in Organic Chemistry*, Cornell University Press, Ithaca, N.Y., 1953, Chap. V.

9. See F. Basolo and R. G. Pearson, *Mechanisms of Inorganic Reactions*, Wiley, New York, 1958, Chap. 3.
10. E. D. Hughes, C. K. Ingold, and R. I. Reed, *J. Chem. Soc.*, **1950**, 2400.
11. L. Melander, *Arkiv. Kemi*, **2**, 213 (1950).
12. J. F. Bunnett, E. W. Garbisch, and K. M. Pruitt, *J. Am. Chem. Soc.*, **79**, 385 (1957).
13. G. A. Olah and S. J. Kuhn, *J. Am. Chem. Soc.*, **80**, 6535, 6540 (1958).
14. Such usage is not identical with Ingold's definition of nucleophile (see Ref. 1). In Ingold's usage, all the reactions we discuss are nucleophilic substitutions. We conform to the looser definition because the concept of nucleophile is most useful in contexts such as discussion of the relative reactivities of entering groups (nucleophilicity orders). See C. G. Swain and C. B. Scott, *J. Am. Chem. Soc.*, **75**, 141 (1953) and J. O. Edwards and R. G. Pearson, *ibid.*, **84**, 16 (1962).
15. R. G. Pearson, H. B. Gray, and F. Basolo, *J. Am. Chem. Soc.*, **82**, 787 (1960).

chapter	# Square-Planar
two	# Substitutions

This chapter is devoted to a discussion of the substitution mechanisms of square-planar complexes. Although the term *square-planar complex* requires D_{4h} symmetry in the strictest sense, we shall use the term to designate any four-coordinate complex in which the central metal atom, and the four attached donor atoms lie approximately in the same plane.

2-1 MODEL FOR SQUARE-PLANAR SUBSTITUTIONS

Steric Course

Of the important metal-complex geometries, the square-planar structure is best suited for substitutions by a pathways, since there are two coordination positions open for the attack of an incoming group. From purely steric considerations, the geometry of the transition state is expected to be approximately trigonal bipyramidal, since this arrangement minimizes the mutual repulsions of the five ligands. A square-pyramidal structure is another reasonable possibility for the transition state. It should be noted, however, that the difference between an "approximate trigonal bipyramid" and an "approximate square pyramid" may be vanishingly small.

Since the steric factors are so favorable for associative activation, we shall develop an A mechanism via a trigonal-bipyramidal intermediate as the most reasonable *model* for square-planar substitutions. This process is shown in Figure 2-1. Although a two-step stoichiometric A mechanism may not operate in every case, the five-coordinate intermediate should serve as a useful model of the *transition state* in substitutions which are better designated I_a.

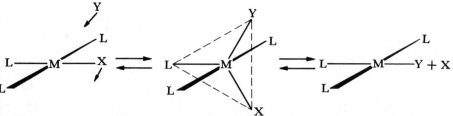

Figure 2-1   *Associative* **A** *mechanism for square-planar substitutions via a trigonal-bipyramidal intermediate.*

Orbital Course

The energy-level ordering in square-planar complexes continues to be a subject in which there is much interest and some disagreement.[1-13]   The relative energies of the molecular orbitals (MO's) pertinent to our discussion are known with reasonable certainty, however.   An MO-level scheme is presented in Figure 2-2.

In $PtCl_4^{2-}$, for example, the σ- and π-bonding electrons undoubtedly are delocalized over all five atoms.   Since the chlorine-valence orbitals are more stable than the platinum-valence orbitals, the bonding electrons are "pulled" toward the chlorine atoms.   The antibonding MO's derived from the d-valence orbitals consist of four relatively stable orbitals (π_{xy}^*, $\sigma_{z^2}^*$, $\pi_{xz,yz}^*$) and one relatively unstable orbital, the strongly antibonding $\sigma_{x^2-y^2}^*$.   The ordering of the π^* orbitals is established as $\pi_{xy}^* > \pi_{xz,yz}^*$, but the placement of $\sigma_{z^2}^*$ is an unsettled matter.   A recent interpretation [13] places $\sigma_{z^2}^*$ below $\pi_{xz,yz}^*$ for $PtCl_4^{2-}$, although for $Ni(CN)_4^{2-}$ it appears [11] that $\sigma_{z^2}^*$ is above $\pi_{xz,yz}^*$.   The $\sigma_{x^2-y^2}^*$ MO is composed mainly of the $d_{x^2-y^2}$ orbital, which is directed at the four ligands.   The four relatively stable metal(d)-based orbitals are occupied in $PtCl_4^{2-}$, whereas $\sigma_{x^2-y^2}^*$ is empty in the ground state.   At higher energy, we find the p_z valence orbital, a π-symmetry orbital, *not* involved in σ bonding, and the strongly antibonding, unstable orbitals σ_s^*, σ_x^*, and σ_y^*.

A particularly good electronic structural arrangement for the square-planar situation should be d^8 low-spin; in this case, maximum use is made of the relatively stable metal(d)-based orbitals.   This is borne out by experiment, because the majority of square-planar transition metal complexes, and all square-planar complexes of interest in our mechanistic discussion here, contain d^8 central metal ions and are diamagnetic.

Since the p_z valence orbital in square-planar metal complexes is not involved in σ bonding, it is available for forming the extra σ bond required in associative activation processes.   The ready availability of a valence

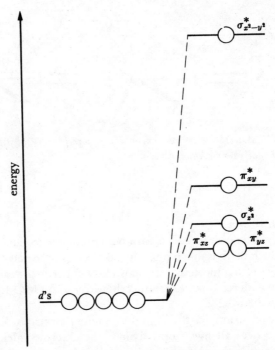

Figure 2-2   *Assumed ordering of the antibonding MO's derived from d valence orbitals in a square-planar metal complex.*

orbital to attach the additional ligand present in the proposed five-coordinate intermediate indicates that, from electronic structural considerations, square-planar substitutions most probably should proceed by an associative **A** mechanism. It is significant that many d^8 low-spin complexes, for example, $Fe(CO)_5$, are five-coordinate.[75] In these cases the proposed five-coordinate intermediate of an **A** mechanism for d^8 square-planar complexes is the *ground state*. A very deep minimum in the potential-energy surface corresponding to the five-coordinate d^8 complex is a reality in these situations.

From simple electronic-structural considerations, both the trigonal-bipyramidal and square-pyramidal geometries are possible for the proposed five-coordinate intermediate. In a trigonal bipyramid (see Figure 2-3) metal nd_{z^2}, $(n+1)s$, $(n+1)p_x$, $(n+1)p_y$, and $(n+1)p_z$ orbitals are involved in strong σ bonding; in a square pyramid, $nd_{x^2-y^2}$, $[nd_{z^2} + (n+1)s]$, $(n+1)p_x$, $(n+1)p_y$, and $(n+1)p_z$ orbitals are involved in strong σ bonding. Probable relative MO energies for these structures are shown in Figure 2-4.

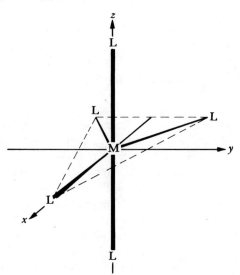

Figure 2-3   *Coordinate system for MO's in a trigonal bipyramid.*

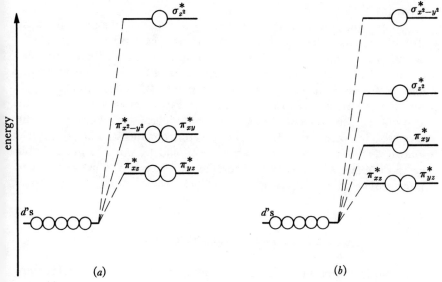

Figure 2-4   *Assumed ordering of the antibonding MO's derived from d valence orbitals in (a) a trigonal-bipyramidal complex and (b) in a square-pyramidal complex.*

The square pyramidal d^8 system would have the configuration $[\pi^*_{xz,yz}]^4$ $[\pi^*_{xy}]^2[\sigma^*_{z^2}]^2$; notice that there are two electrons in a pure σ^*-type orbital. From the trigonal-bipyramidal MO-level scheme, the electronic structure of the d^8 five-coordinate intermediate would be $[\pi^*_{xz,yz}]^4[\pi^*_{x^2-y^2,xy}]^4$, with no electrons in strongly σ^* MO's. As indicated above, this is expected to be a relatively stable intermediate structure, with five σ bonds. Ligands with relatively stable, empty π orbitals (π-acceptor ligands) such as CO are able to stabilize the $\pi^*_{x^2-y^2,xy}$ and $\pi^*_{xz,yz}$ levels through metal $\rightarrow$ ligand π bonding. A complicating feature is that the $x^2 - y^2$ and xy orbitals are involved to some extent in the σ-molecular orbital system, and the level labeled $\pi^*_{x^2-y^2,xy}$ is destabilized through this σ interaction. Thus there are many energy factors (including the energies of the σ-bonding levels), which at present we are not able to assess in a quantitative manner, and we conclude that *a choice between the trigonal bipyramid and the square pyramid cannot be made on electronic-structural grounds alone*. However, there is an indication that the trigonal-bipyramidal structure is electronically favored for a d^8 low-spin complex containing good π-acceptor ligands. We shall outline the orbital course of square substitution in considerable detail for an **A** mechanism with a trigonal-bipyramidal intermediate in the section on the *trans*-effect.

Summary Statement

Simple but pertinent theoretical arguments lead to the following conclusion regarding the mechanism by which free ligands exchange for bound ligands in d^8 square-planar complexes: From both steric and electronic considerations, an associative **A** mechanism is expected to be the most useful *model* for discussion of square-planar (d^8) substitutions. Such reactions are strongly expected to have at least **a** activation, and thus be **I**$_a$ if not **A**. Steric factors favor a trigonal-bipyramidal structure for the proposed intermediate. If we extrapolate from the stability of several known d^8 five-coordinate complexes, it should be possible in favorable cases to obtain kinetic evidence for the existence of the five-coordinate intermediate of an **A** process.

2-2   RATE LAW AND STEREOCHEMISTRY

First, it is important to note that substitution reactions of Pt(II) complexes proceed with retention of geometric configuration; that is, *trans* complexes give *trans* products and *cis* complexes give *cis* products.[14, 18]

It is now generally recognized that most square-planar substitution reactions in solution follow a two-term rate law [Eq. (2-1)], where k_1 is a

$$\text{rate} = \frac{-d\,[\text{complex}]}{dt} = (k_1 + k_2[\text{Y}])[\text{complex}] \qquad (2\text{-}1)$$

first-order rate constant, k_2 is a second-order rate constant, [Y] represents the concentration of the entering ligand, and [complex] the concentration of the complex.

The rate law (2-1) is clearly shown by the observed [15,39] kinetics of the reactions in aqueous solution of Pt(dien)Br$^+$ with several entering groups, including OH$^-$, Cl$^-$, I$^-$, NO$_2^-$, and SCN$^-$ Pseudo first-order rate constants k_{obs} for these reactions were determined at various concentrations of the entering ligand Y. The plots of k_{obs} versus [Y] are shown in Figure 2-5. In the concentration ranges studied, the plots are linear with approximately equal, nonzero intercepts. The slopes of the lines give the various k_2's and the intercepts give the k_1's.

The "k_2 term" ($k_2[\text{Y}][\text{complex}]$) in the rate law [Eq. (2-1)] is in agreement with the theoretical considerations of Section 2-1, since we expect a second-order rate law for an **A** mechanism. On the other hand, the appearance of a first-order term ($k_1[\text{complex}]$) is at first sight disturb-

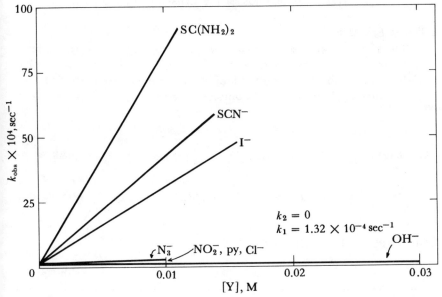

Figure 2-5 *Relative reactivities of different entering groups with Pt(dien)Br$^+$ in aqueous solution at 25°C. See Table 2-7.*

ing, and indicates the possibility of a duality of mechanism, this term representing a path of a dissociative variety. However, no mechanism other than **a** need be invoked, since the k_1 term can arise logically from an associative mechanism involving specifically one molecule of solvent as reactant, in which case we rewrite Eq. (2-1) as follows Eq. (2-2).

$$\text{rate} = (k_s[S] + k_2[Y])[\text{complex}] \quad \text{(with } k_1 = k_s[S]) \quad (2\text{-}2)$$

The experimental rate law is thus compatible with an **a** mechanism for planar substitution, but the k_1 term could be due to a dissociative process. In the discussion of the experiments that follow, we shall see that, for unhindered square-planar complexes, the evidence overwhelmingly points to a mechanism involving associative activation for both the k_1 and k_2 terms in the rate law, hence either an **A** or $\mathbf{I_a}$ process.

Square-planar complexes with Pt(II) as central atom are best suited for conventional quantitative kinetic studies, because of their stabilities and relative inertness. Thus, we shall first discuss the substantial amount of information on relative rates of substitutions in Pt(II) complexes; [15–20, 22–47, 51, 62, 64, 77–79, 81–83, 87] this information provides a detailed view of the *intimate* mechanism.

2-3 EFFECT OF LIGANDS IN THE COMPLEX ON THE RATE

Trans Effect

The kinetic *trans* effect in square-planar substitutions, first recognized by Werner [48] and elaborated on by Chernyaev, [49] refers to the special effects of *trans* substituents on the lability of a leaving group. Of all the specific ligand effects in metal complex substitution reactions, the *trans*

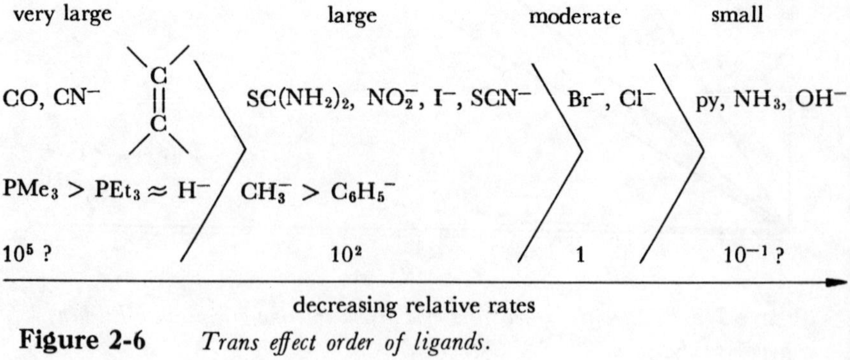

Figure 2-6   *Trans effect order of ligands.*

Table 2-1   *Trans-effect in Pt(II)*
substitution reactions [a]
trans-$Pt(PEt_3)_2(L)Cl + py \rightleftharpoons$
trans-$Pt(PEt_3)_2(L)(py)^+ + Cl^-$

L	k_{obs}, sec^{-1} [b]	t, °C
PMe$_3$ [c]	2×10^{-1}	0
H$^-$	4.7×10^{-2}	0
PEt$_3$ [d]	4.1×10^{-2}	0
Me$^-$	6.0×10^{-4}	25
C$_6$H$_5^-$	1.2×10^{-4}	25
Cl$^-$	3.5×10^{-6}	25

[a] Data from Ref. 17.   Rates in ethanol; [py] = 0.006 M.
[b] Approach to equilibrium is a pseudo first-order process.
Here k_{obs} is the measured pseudo first-order rate constant.
[c] Complex is *cis*-$Pt(PMe_3)_2Cl_2$.
[d] Complex is *cis*-$Pt(PEt_3)_2Cl_2$.

effect is probably the most dramatic, spanning several orders of magnitude in rate.

Although the *trans*-effect order of ligands is undoubtedly dependent to some extent on the substrate, the generally accepted "average" order is [18, 43, 50, 51] as in Figure 2-6.   The relative positions of PMe$_3$, PEt$_3$, H$^-$, Me$^-$, and C$_6$H$_5^-$ were determined from the measured [17] rates in ethanol solution of reaction (2-3).   A comparison of the rates of reaction (2-3) is

$$Pt(PR_3)_2(L)Cl + py \rightleftharpoons Pt(PR_3)_2(py)(L)^+ + Cl^- \qquad (2-3)$$

given in Table 2-1.   For the substrate *cis*-$Pt(NH_3)(L)Cl_2^{n-}$, the relative rates in aqueous solution for replacement of the Cl$^-$ *trans* to L are C_2H_4 = *very large* $\gg$ NO$_2^-$ = 9 > Br$^-$ = 3 > Cl$^-$ = 1.[29]

There have been many papers written on the theory of the *trans* effect.[18, 52-60]   Notable theories are the electrostatic-polarization theory of Grinberg [52] and the π-bonding theory of Chatt et al.,[57, 58] and Orgel.[59] Until it was found that H$^-$ has a very large *trans* effect, the π-bonding theory accounted reasonably well for the over-all ligand order.   It now seems clear, however, that both σ- and π-electronic effects are important, and thus we present here a combined σ- and π-MO explanation of the *trans* effect.

σ-*Trans Effect*

Of the four metal valence orbitals involved in strong σ bonding in a square-planar complex, only the p orbitals have *trans* directional properties.

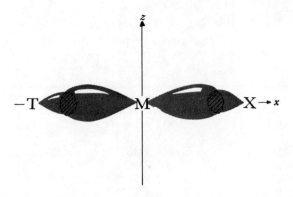

Figure 2-7   *Bonding of the trans (T) and leaving (X) groups with one p_σ orbital.*

That is, the *trans* group and the leaving group must share the same p orbital (and average of $\frac{1}{2}p$ orbital for each ligand) in the over-all σ-MO structure, as shown in Figure 2-7.   If the *trans* group has a particularly strong σ interaction with the p orbital, the bond to the leaving group may be relatively weaker in the ground state.   The driving force is then to provide more p orbital to the *trans* group by moving the leaving group out of the region of strong overlap while the entering group moves in, as shown schematically in Figure 2-8.   The available p_z orbital is used to help attach both the entering group and the leaving group to the central metal in the five-coordinate transition state.   Since the entering and

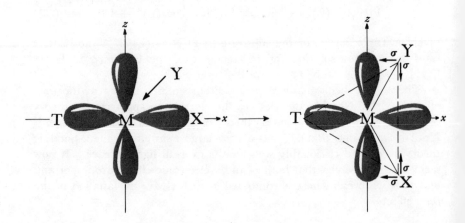

Figure 2-8   *Change in the metal p_σ orbital structure in square-planar substitution.*

leaving groups now share the available p_z orbital, the *trans* group *owns* much more than one-half the p_x orbital in the transition state. This means that the difference in the energies of the ground and transition states should be relatively small for good $\sigma \rightarrow$ metal(p) donor ligands. Calculations summarized in Table 2-2 show that the available valence orbitals of the ligands H^-, PR_3, and Me^- have unusually large overlap with a Pt $6p_\sigma$ orbital. We conclude that H^-, PR_3, and Me^- have large σ-*trans* effects and that over-all high *trans*-effects of $-SCN^-$ and I^- are principally due to substantial σ-effect contributions.

It is not to be implied from the above discussion that the bond to the *trans* group be necessarily stronger in the transition state than in the ground state. In fact, both the leaving group and the *trans* group may

Table 2-2 *Relative σ- and π-trans effects of ligands*

Estimated σ-effect order [a]

$H^- > PR_3 > -SCN^- > I^-, CH_3^-, CO, CN^- > Br^- > Cl^- > NH_3 > OH^-$

Estimated π-effect order [b]

$, CO > CN^- > -NO_2^- > -SCN^- >$

$I^- > Br^- > Cl^- > NH_3 > OH^-$

[a] Relative positions estimated from the values of the overlap integrals $S(6p_\sigma, np_\sigma)$ between a Pt $6p_\sigma$ orbital and appropriate ligand p_σ valence orbitals. Analytical radial functions for Pt were calculated by H. Basch. Ligand atom radial functions from E. Clementi, *J. Chem. Phys.*, **40**, 1944 (1964). Bond distances were estimated from covalent radii. Actual values of the σ overlap integrals are $S(6p,1s_H) = 0.5169$; $S(6p,3p_P) = 0.3770$; $S(6p,3p_S) = 0.3574$; $S(6p,2p_C) = 0.3494$; $S(6p,4p_{Br}) = 0.3357$; $S(6p,3p_{Cl}) = 0.3332$; $S(6p,2p_N) = 0.3169$; $S(6p,2p_O) = 0.2877$. The position of I^- is a reasonable guess.

[b] The ligands CO, , CN^-, NO_2^-, and SCN^- have reasonably stable,

empty π^* molecular orbitals. The relative positions within this first group were estimated from the values of the overlap integrals $S(5d_\pi, \pi^*)$. The necessary Pt $5d$ functions and the ligand π^* functions were calculated by H. Basch and D. Gutterman. Actual values of the π overlap integrals are as follows: $S(5d,\pi^*C_2H_4) = 0.096$; $S(5d, \pi^*CO) = 0.093$; $S(5d,\pi^*CN^-) = 0.088$; $S(5d,\pi^*NO_2^-) = 0.066$; $S(5d,\pi^*-SCN^-) = 0.052$. As a group, the ligands I^-, Br^-, Cl^-, NH_3, and OH^- are rated lower in π-*trans* effect, because their lowest available π orbitals are believed to be considerably less stable than those of the ligands in the first group. The suggested ordering of decreasing π-*trans* effect in this second group parallels the estimated ordering of decreasing stability of the lowest available π orbital of the ligands in question.

be loosened in the transition state, owing to the presence of the entering group. Falk and Halpern have studied [81] reaction (2-3) with the L *trans*-groups H^- and D^-. There is a large secondary kinetic isotope effect, corresponding to a decrease in the second-order rate constant by a factor of approximately 1.4 when hydride is replaced by deuteride. The slower rate in the case of *trans*-$Pt(PEt_3)_2(D)Cl$ is interpreted as a weakening of the Pt-H(Pt-D) binding in a five-coordinate transition state.

π-*Trans Effect*

In a square-planar complex, three d orbitals have proper symmetries for π interaction, xy, xz, and yz. Of these, the xz and yz orbitals interact only with both members of a pair of *trans*-disposed ligands. Assuming the coordinate system shown in Figure 2-9, we see that the xz orbital is shared by the *trans* ligand and the *leaving* ligand. On formation of the trigonal bipyramid, four d orbitals are of the right symmetries for π interaction, namely, xz, yz, $x^2 - y^2$, and xy. It is significant that all these orbitals are shared in π interaction with the ligands in the *trigonal plane:* that is, the *trans* group, the entering group, and the leaving group. In d^8 complexes, furthermore, all the $d(\pi^*)$ orbitals are filled. Thus the trigonal-bipyramidal transition state is greatly stabilized if the *trans* group possesses empty, reasonably stable, π-symmetry orbitals, since an interaction of empty ligand π orbitals with the filled $d(\pi^*)$ orbitals delocalizes electronic charge to the *trans* ligand and lowers the energy of the system. In simple terms, the *trans* ligand helps to accommodate the excess electronic charge added to the central metal by the entering ligand. Thus, the effect of a good π-acceptor *trans* group is to lower the over-all activation energy; this

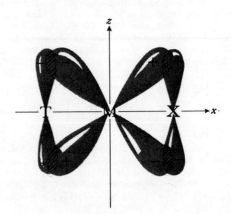

Figure 2-9   *π-interaction of the trans xz orbital with the trans (T) and leaving (X) groups.*

we take to be the π-*trans* effect. It should be noted that the two *cis* ligands, which occupy axial positions in the trigonal bipyramid, only interact in π bonding with two of the four $d(\pi^*)$ orbitals (the xz and yz). It follows that the *cis* ligands cannot be as helpful as the *trans* ligand in lowering the activation energy by metal $\rightarrow$ ligand π bonding.

An attempt to assess the σ- and π-*trans* effects of several important ligands is given in Table 2-2. The ratings are based on the overlaps of appropriate ligand valence orbitals with Pt $5d_\pi$ (π-*trans* effect) and $6p_\sigma$ (σ-*trans* effect) orbitals. Ligands that are very high in π-*trans* effect are

CO, CN⁻, and $\text{C}=\text{C}$. The ligand $-NO_2^-$ probably has a large π-*trans*

effect, but exhibits only a weak σ-*trans* effect in comparison with CO and CN⁻. This is the suggested explanation of the over-all order CO, CN⁻ $\gg -NO_2^-$.

A very interesting nmr study of the complexes *trans*-$Pt(PEt_3)_2$-(p-FC_6H_4)X and *trans*-$Pt(PEt_3)_2(m$-$FC_6H_4)$X has been reported [61] in which the chemical shifts of the *meta* and *para* F's relative to fluorobenzene are compared for various X groups. The chemical shifts of the *meta* F supposedly are due to σ-donor effects of the X groups, whereas the shifts of the *para* F logically are due to a combination of σ- and π-effects. The study supports a *trans*-effect theory based on two electronic effects, since both *meta* and *para* F's are strongly shielded with X⁻ = Me⁻ (large σ-donor effect); the Z parameter ($Z = para$ shift $- meta$ shift) is smallest for X = CN⁻, indicating substantial π-acceptor interaction in this case. However, extreme caution must be exercised in relating nmr data to the *kinetic trans* effect. It is almost certain that the chemical shifts are due to the combined effects of many orbital interactions, not just the *trans*-directed ones. For example, in the σ system alone, the ligands $FC_6H_4^-$ and X⁻ share the valence orbitals $nd_{x^2-y^2}$, nd_{z^2}, $(n+1)s$, and one np_σ. Only the np_σ orbital is involved in the σ-*trans* effect, but all the others must contribute to the chemical shifts of the *meta* and *para* F's. Furthermore, the nmr experiment is not capable of testing the *change* in p_σ-donor interaction and the *change* in $d(\pi^*)$ interaction in going to the transition state. These are perhaps the two most important quantities in the kinetic *trans* effect.

Effect of Cis Ligands

In contrast to the profound influence on substitution rates of the group *trans* to the leaving group, the *cis* groups have only a very small effect. Grinberg [32] has pointed out that pyridine substitutes a little faster in $Pt(py)Cl_3^-$ than in $Pt(NH_3)Cl_3^-$ and, in comparing NH_3 and NO_2^-, that a leaving Cl⁻ is slightly more labile with NH_3 *cis*. This gives the *cis* effect order py $> NH_3 > NO_2^-$ for the substrates involved.

Table 2-3   *Effect of ligand cis to the leaving group*
in Pt(II) substitution reactions

csi-Pt(PEt$_3$)$_2$(L)Cl + py $\rightleftharpoons$ cis-Pt(PEt$_3$)$_2$(X)(py)$^+$ + Cl$^-$ ^{a}	
L$^-$	$k_{obs} \times 10^2$, sec^{-1} ^{b}
Cl$^-$	4.17
C$_6$H$_5^-$	7.92
Me$^-$	11.4

$trans$-PtL$_2$Cl$_2$ + ^{36}Cl$^-$ $\rightleftharpoons$ $trans$-PtL$_2$^{36}Cl$_2$ + Cl$^-$ ^{c}	
L	$k_2 \times 10^4$, M^{-1} sec^{-1} ^{d}
Piperidine	9.25
AsEt$_3$	6.9
PEt$_3$	0.29
S(s-Bu)$_2$	0.74

^{a} [py] = 0.0062 M in methanol solution, 25°C.
^{b} Data from Ref. 17.
^{c} Methanol solution at 30°C; μ = 0.1.
^{d} Data from Ref. 22.

Since this is the inverted *trans*-effect order of these ligands, it has been suggested [18] that a good *trans*-effect group may be low in *cis* effect. This is probably not a good generalization, considering the rate data in Table 2-3. We see that there is no significant difference in the rates of pyridine substitution in *cis*-Pt(PEt$_3$)$_2$(L)Cl complexes, with less than a factor of three spanning the L order Me$^-$ > C$_6$H$_5^-$ > Cl$^-$. For comparison, recall that the *trans*-effect order of these ligands is also Me$^-$ > C$_6$H$_5^-$ > Cl$^-$, but relative rates are 165:35:1. In addition, it is not possible to relate large *trans* effects with small *cis* effects in the associative Cl$^-$ reaction with *trans*-PtL$_2$Cl$_2$ complexes (see Table 2-3). The order of k_2's for different L's is piperidine > AsEt$_3$ > S(s-Bu)$_2$ > PEt$_3$, with k_2 of the bis-piperidine complex larger than k_2 of the bis-PEt$_3$ complex by a factor of 30. However, the bis-piperidine complex and the bis-AsEt$_3$ complex have about the same value of k_2(Cl$^-$). The *trans*-effect difference of these ligands is probably about 10^5 in rate, with AsEt$_3$, PEt$_3$, $\gg$ piperidine. We conclude that *cis* effects are small and do not follow any regular pattern with respect to *trans* effects.

Tucker and co-workers have shown that *cis* effects can be more important than *trans* effects when comparing groups of nearly equal *trans* effect.[16] In substitutions in the chloroammine Pt(II) complexes, it was found that the difference in the *cis* effects of NH$_3$ and Cl$^-$ (NH$_3$ > Cl$^-$)

is *larger* than their *trans*-effect difference ($Cl^- > NH_3$). Therefore, the *cis* ligands determine the relative substitution rates in these complexes.

Steric Effects

The first compelling experimental evidence for associative activation in square-planar substitution was the demonstration of large rate effects on blocking the entering-group attack positions above and below the plane.[17] The results of a study of the rates of reaction of various (*cis*- and *trans*-) $Pt(PEt_3)_2(R)Cl$ complexes with pyridine in ethanol solution are given in Table 2-4.

The study shows the relative rates for zero, one, and two potential coordination positions blocked with *o*-methyl groups on the aromatic rings. Consistent with associative activation, the over-all rate decreases sharply for both *cis* and *trans* blocking, proceeding from no positions blocked (R = phenyl) to two positions blocked (R = mesityl).

Direct evidence for an approximately trigonal-bipyramidal geometry for the transition state is the fact that *cis* blocking is more effective than *trans* blocking. As shown in Figure 2-10 a trigonal-bipyramidal transition state is greatly strained by *cis* blocking (that is, in apical positions the blocking groups are forced closer to the entering and leaving groups), but

Table 2-4   *Steric effects in Pt(II) substitution reactions [a] in ethanol solution*

$$Pt(PEt_3)_2(R)Cl + py \rightleftharpoons$$
$$Pt(PEt_3)_2(R)(py)^+ + Cl^-$$

Ligand R	Relative rates [b]	
	R *trans* to Cl	R *cis* to Cl
Mesityl	1	1
o-Tolyl	5	200
Phenyl	36	80,000

[a] From Ref. 17.

[b] Actual rates for reactions with 0.0062 M py are as follows: *cis* complexes at 0°; $k_{obs} = 8.0 \times 10^{-2} sec^{-1}$ for R = phenyl; $k_{obs} = 2.0 \times 10^{-4} sec^{-1}$ for R = *o*-tolyl; $k_{obs} = 1.0 \times 10^{-6} sec^{-1}$ for R = mesityl; *trans* complexes at 25°; $k_{obs} = 1.24 \times 10^{-4} sec^{-1}$ for R = phenyl; $k_{obs} = 1.70 \times 10^{-5} sec^{-1}$ for R = *o*-tolyl; $k_{obs} = 3.42 \times 10^{-6} sec^{-1}$ for R = mesityl. See footnote *b*, Table 2-1 for explanation of k_{obs} for these reversible reactions.

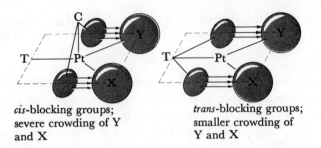

Figure 2-10   *Effect of cis and trans blocking groups on the stability of a trigonal-bipyramidal transition state.*

not nearly so crowded by *trans* blocking.   The experimental results are in complete accord with this, since *cis* blocking causes the relative rate to drop by $1/80{,}000$ from R $=$ phenyl to R $=$ mesityl, whereas *trans* blocking only causes a drop of $\frac{1}{36}$.

Some other good examples of steric effects on the rate of planar substitution are summarized in Table 2-5.   The fact that the k_1 path of ^{36}Cl$^-$ exchange for *cis*-Pt(α-pic)$_2$Cl$_2$ is only $\frac{1}{20}$ as fast as the k_1 path for *cis*-Pt(4-ampy)$_2$Cl$_2$ in ethanol solution is strong evidence that the k_1 term represents an associative pathway involving the solvent.

A very striking example of the large steric effect on the rate of planar substitution is the comparison of the rates of reaction of Pt(dien)Cl$^+$ and Pt(Et$_4$dien)Cl$^+$ in aqueous solution.   In the latter complex the four ethyl groups on the terminal nitrogens hover above and below the plane and block access to the central metal.   *It is significant that the hindered complex*

Table 2-5   *Steric effects in substitution reactions of Pt(II) complexes containing amine ligands* [a]

Complex	Entering group	Solvent	$k_1 \times 10^6$, sec^{-1}
cis-Pt(4-ampy)$_2$Cl$_2$	^{36}Cl$^-$	EtOH	11.0 [b]
cis-Pt(α-pic)$_2$Cl$_2$	^{36}Cl$^-$	EtOH	0.48 [b]
Pt(dien)Cl$^+$	Br$^-$	H$_2$O	100 [c]
Pt(Et$_4$dien)Cl$^+$	Br$^-$	H$_2$O	8.5 [d]

[a] Reactions at 25°C.
[b] From Ref. 38.
[c] From Ref. 15.
[d] At 80°; k_1 is very small at 25°; from Ref. 62.

reacts several orders of magnitude slower than the unhindered one. Apparently, *both* k_1 and k_2 terms are drastically affected, once again strongly suggesting an associative mechanism for unhindered systems. Indeed, there is no k_2 term in the reactions of entering groups with Pt(Et$_4$dien)Cl$^+$, which indicates that there is no mechanism of **a** type available, and the rate of 8.5×10^{-6} sec^{-1} probably represents a dissociative process. We thus estimate that for unhindered Pt(dien)Cl$^+$ the associative reaction with solvent water is faster than the dissociative path at 25° by a factor of at least 10^4.

Leaving Group

In the final section on rate effects due to ligands in the complex, we take up the important effect of the leaving group. A fairly extensive study of relative leaving-group rates has been made, utilizing the reaction [34] of Eq. (2-4). In this case the three other coordination positions are rendered

$$\text{Pt(dien)X}^+ + \text{pyridine} \rightarrow \text{Pt(dien)(py)}^{2+} + \text{X}^- \qquad (2\text{-}4)$$

inert by using the strongly complexing dien ligand, and the entering ligand is always pyridine. Thus, the rate effect of only one variable, X$^-$, is investigated. The rates in aqueous solution obtained from reaction (2-4) are given in Table 2-6. The order of decreasing rates is NO$_3^-$ > H$_2$O > Cl$^-$ > Br$^-$ > I$^-$ > N$_3^-$ > —SCN$^-$ > —NO$_2^-$ > CN$^-$.

Table 2-6 *Rates of different leaving groups for reactions in water at 25° [a]*

Pt(dien)X$^+$ + py $\rightarrow$

Pt(dien)(py)$^{2+}$ + X$^-$

Leaving group X	$k_{obs} \times 10^6$, sec^{-1}
NO$_3^-$	Reaction very fast
H$_2$O	1900 [b]
Cl$^-$	35
Br$^-$	23
I$^-$	10
N$_3^-$	0.83
SCN$^-$	0.30
NO$_2^-$	0.050
CN$^-$	0.017

[a] [py] = 0.0059 M; from Ref. 34.
[b] For 0.005 M pyridine; from Ref. 20.

First we note that there is a substantial difference in the relative rates of different leaving groups.   This indicates that a considerable perturbation of the M—X bond occurs in forming the transition state, at least in the complexes with strongly bonded leaving groups.   In this connection, it is significant that the order of labilities parallels the order of aqueous solution instabilities of these complexes; that is, we have:

$$\text{rates:} \quad \text{Pt(dien)I}^+ < \text{Pt(dien)Br}^+ < \text{Pt(dien)Cl}^+$$

$$\begin{array}{l} \text{formation} \\ \text{constants:} \end{array} \quad \text{Pt(dien)I}^+ > \text{Pt(dien)Br}^+ > \text{Pt(dien)Cl}^+$$

Also, it is interesting to note that the leaving groups high in the *trans*-effect series are very slowly replaced.   This is consistent with the combined σ- and π-*trans*-effect theory, since the theory suggests that good *trans*-effect groups will be strongly bonded to the metal.   However, the reverse need not be true; that is, a poor *trans* labilizer should not always be rapidly displaced.   For example, OH$^-$ is a very poor *trans* labilizer, but it is very difficult to dislodge.   Thus the strength of a Pt—OH bond is probably not derived from strong σ interaction with a Pt $6p_\sigma$ orbital, but more likely from good Pt($5d$)—OH σ bonding.   Good σ bonding to d-valence orbitals does not result in a *trans* effect.   Another poor *trans* labilizer that is an inert leaving group is NH$_3$.   In the reaction of Pt(NH$_3$)$_4^{2+}$ with ^{15}NH$_3$, no exchange was observed after 217 days.[45]   We conclude that an approximately trigonal-bipyramidal transition state is relatively high energy when ligands such as OH$^-$ and NH$_3$ occupy one or more positions in the trigonal plane.

2-4   EFFECT OF THE ENTERING GROUP ON THE RATE

One of the most important requirements of an associative mechanism is that there be large differences in the reactivities of different entering groups.   Numerous investigations [15, 19, 20, 22–24, 33, 47, 77–79, 82, 83] have established that this is indeed the case in square-planar Pt(II) substitutions.   Values of the second-order rate constant in aqueous solution for reaction [15] (2-5) are given in Table 2-7.   The order of ligands in decreas-

$$\text{Pt(dien)Br}^+ + \text{Y}^- \rightarrow \text{Pt(dien)Y}^+ + \text{Br}^- \qquad (2\text{-}5)$$

ing k_2 values is SC(NH$_2$)$_2$ > SCN$^-$ > I$^-$ > N$_3^-$ > NO$_2^-$ > py > Cl$^-$ > OH$^-$ for this substrate.

A thorough study of reactions of different ligands with several substrates, especially *trans*-Pt(py)$_2$Cl$_2$, in methanol solution has been reported.[22]   The k_2 values are summarized in Table 2-8.   For *trans*-

Table 2-7 *Second-order rate constants for substitution reactions of Pt(dien)Br$^+$ in water at 25° [a]*

Pt(dien)Br$^+$ + Y$^-$ → Pt(dien)Y$^+$ + Br$^-$	
Y$^-$	$k_2 \times 10^4$, M^{-1} sec^{-1}
OH$^-$	0
Cl$^-$	8.8
I$^-$	2300
py	33
NO$_2^-$	37
N$_3^-$	77
SCN$^-$	4300
SC(NH$_2$)$_2$	8300

[a] From Ref. 15.

Table 2-8 *Second-order rate constants for substitution reactions of trans-Pt(py)$_2$Cl$_2$ complexes in methanol at 30° [a]*

trans-Pt(py)$_2$Cl$_2$ + Y → trans-Pt(py)$_2$(Cl)Y + Cl$^-$	
Y	$k_2 \times 10^3$, M^{-1} sec^{-1}
MeO$^-$	0.1
^{36}Cl$^-$	.45 [b]
NH$_3$	.47
py	.55
NO$_2^-$	.68
N$_3^-$	1.55
NH$_2$OH	2.9
N$_2$H$_4$	2.93
Br$^-$	3.7
C$_6$H$_5$SH	5.7
SO$_3^{2-}$	250
I$^-$	107
SCN$^-$	180
SeCN$^-$	5150
C$_6$H$_5$S$^-$	6000
SC(NH$_2$)$_2$	6000
S$_2$O$_3^{2-}$	9000

[a] k_1(MeOH) = 1 × 10^{-5} sec^{-1}. From Ref. 22.
[b] Estimated from data on *trans*-Pt(pip)$_2$Cl$_2$.

$Pt(py)_2Cl_2$, we have the reactivity order $S_2O_3^{2-} > SC(NH_2)_2, C_6H_5S^- >$ $SeCN^- \gg SO_3^{2-} > SCN^- > I^- \gg C_6H_5SH > Br^- > N_2H_4, NH_2OH >$ $N_3^- > NO_2^- > py > NH_3 > Cl^- > MeO^-$.

Combining these two detailed studies with semiquantitative observations of the reactivities of CO, CN^-, C_2H_4,[83] and PR_3 in planar substitutions, we estimate the average reactivity order of Figure 2-11 for a representative group of ligands. The average ligand-reactivity order bears a remarkable resemblance to the *trans*-effect order. Thus a good *trans* labilizer is also a good entering group in square-planar substitutions. This is expected for an associative mechanism via a trigonal-bipyramidal intermediate, since the *trans group and the entering group are in similar positions with respect to the leaving group in the trigonal plane*. Whatever stabilization is imparted to the approximately trigonal-bipyramidal transition state by a ligand in *trans* position can also be imparted to some extent when the ligand is in the entering-group position.

A particularly revealing study [20] of entering-group rates involves the substrate $Pt(dien)OH_2^{2+}$, which is presumed to be an intermediate in the k_1 reaction of $Pt(dien)Br^+$ with different Y ligands.

To be consistent with the observed first-order term, $Pt(dien)OH_2^{2+}$ is required to react much faster with Y ligands than the observed k_1 rate. The results given in Table 2-9 show that this requirement is met for every ligand studied. The entering-group reactivity order in aqueous solution with respect to $Pt(dien)OH_2^{2+}$ as substrate is $I^- > SCN^- > Br^- >$ $Cl^- > NO_2^- > py$. Notice that NO_2^- occupies an unusually low position, an interesting fact which will be discussed later.

The very striking, high reactivity of OH^- with $Pt(dien)OH_2^{2+}$ is expected, since in this case no $Pt—OH_2$ bond breaking is necessary, just a rapid proton transfer. Recall that in every case studied in aqueous solution, the rate of replacement of a leaving group by OH^- in a Pt(II) com-

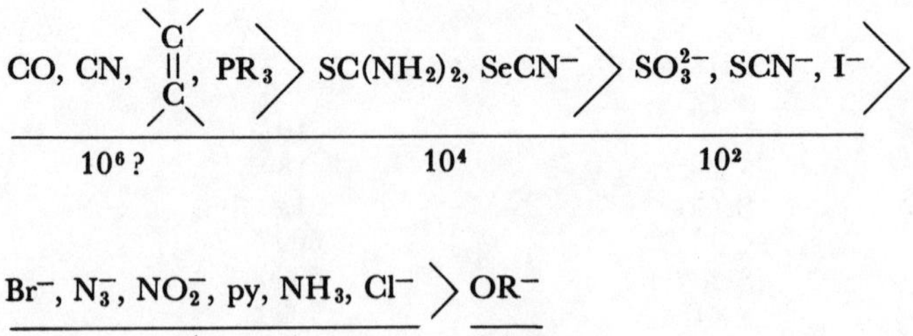

Figure 2-11 *Relative reactivities of different entering groups.*

Table 2-9 *Substitution of water in* $Pt(dien)OH_2^{2+}$ *by various entering groups in aqueous solution at* $25°$ [a]

Entering group	Entering group conc, M	$k_{obs} \times 10^2$, sec^{-1}	Reactivity [b] relative to $Pt(dien)Br^+$
Cl^-	0.005	0.53	50
I^-	0.001	3.9	50
NO_2^-	0.00092	0.090	30
SCN^-	0.001	1.45	20
OH^-	0.005	very large	very large
pyridine	0.005	0.19	100

[a] From Ref. 20.
[b] Expressed as the ratio of k_{obs} for the aquo complex to k_{obs} for the bromo complex, for the same initial concentrations of reactants.

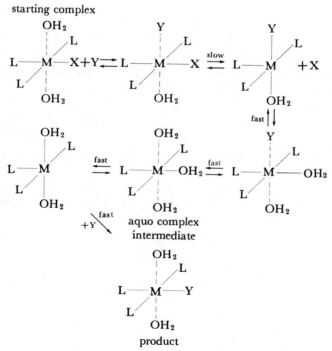

Figure 2-12 *Associative square-pyramidal mechanism for square-planar substitution; see Ref. 14, p. 188.*

plex is completely controlled by the associative reaction with solvent H_2O (the k_1 term; $k_2 = 0$ for OH^-).

The fact that OH^- is 100 per cent efficient in capturing $Pt(dien)OH_2^{2+}$ in solution and at the same time relatively inert toward $Pt(dien)Br^+$ allows a competition experiment to determine whether $Pt(dien)OH_2^{2+}$ is generated in the k_2 path. This test is important, since a very reasonable alternative to the trigonal-bipyramidal mechanism has been proposed. According to the associative-square-pyramidal mechanism of square-planar substitution, the k_2 path is as shown in Figure 2-12. The rate-determining step is still *associative*, as has been established, but the transition state is a square pyramid, from which X dissociates to give an aquo-complex intermediate. The aquo complex would, of course, react rapidly with Y groups in solution to give the product. However, if $Pt(dien)OH_2^{2+}$ is generated by this mechanism and OH^- is present, it will be very rapidly and completely converted to $Pt(dien)OH^+$, which is stable and inert in the presence of most of the Y reagents. According to the associative-trigonal-bipyramidal k_2 path, no $Pt(dien)OH_2^{2+}$ is generated.

Thus, the course of reaction (2-6) in aqueous solution has been studied

$$Pt(dien)Br^+ + Y^- + OH^- \rightarrow ? \qquad (2\text{-}6)$$

in detail.[20, 39] The results are summarized in Table 2-10. In every case studied the first step of reaction (2-6) is the formation of $Pt(dien)Y^+$—*absolutely no $Pt(dien)OH^+$ is formed along the k_2 path.* Further, the $Pt(dien)Y^+$ is formed at its characteristic rate in the absence of OH^-. The next step is the relatively slow conversion of $Pt(dien)Y^+$ to $Pt(dien)OH^+$ at the characteristic k_1 rate of $Pt(dien)Y^+$. Thus, mechanisms of the type shown in Fig. 2-12 involving solvent intervention along the k_2 path, are clearly *not* operative in these cases, and we conclude that the associative **A** mecha-

Table 2-10   *Kinetic results of the reaction of $Pt(dien)X^+$ with different entering groups Y in the presence of OH^- in aqueous solution at 25° [a]*

Starting complex	Y	First product, $k_2 \times 10^4$	$10^4 k_2$ for no OH^-	Final product $k_1 \times 10^4$	Independently measured $k_1 \times 10^4$
$Pt(dien)Cl^+$	Br^-	$Pt(dien)Br^+(50)$	53	$Pt(dien)OH^+(1.32)$	1.32
	I^-	$Pt(dien)I^+(2000)$	2000	$Pt(dien)OH^+(0.42)$	0.42
$Pt(dien)Br^+$	Cl^-	$Pt(dien)Cl^+(9)$	8.8	$Pt(dien)OH^+(1.0)$	1.0
	I^-	$Pt(dien)I^+(2300)$	2300	$Pt(dien)OH^+(0.42)$	0.42

[a] $[OH^-] = 0.001$–0.005 M; from Ref. 39; k_2 values reported in M^{-1} sec^{-1}; k_1 values reported in sec^{-1}.

nism via a trigonal-bipyramidal intermediate (Fig. 2-1) is the best present model for square-planar substitutions.

It is appropriate at this point to summarize the relative entering- and leaving-group effects of different ligands for reactions in which the products are as stable or more stable than the reactants. Probably the best comparison is afforded by reactions in which Cl^- and I^- are the entering and leaving groups.[16] In the reactions of $Pt(dien)Cl^+$ and $Pt(dien)I^+$ with pyridine, the k_2 values show that Cl^- is replaced 3.5 times faster than I^-. For the reactions of $Pt(dien)Cl^+$ with $^{36}Cl^-$ and I^-, the $k_2(I^-)$ is larger than $k_2(^{36}Cl^-)$ by a factor of 40. This illustrates the *greater importance of the entering group* when $\Delta G < 0$, fully consistent with an associative process. This point will be developed further in Section 2-8.

With the results of systematic studies of the effects of *trans*, entering, and leaving groups now established, it is possible to interpret the exchange studies in which all three variables are different in comparing different reactions in aqueous solution. For example, the first quantitative rate study [23] in Pt(II) systems involved the exchange reaction of PtX_4^{2-} with labeled X^- ($X^- = CN^-, I^-, Br^-, Cl^-$). The order of decreasing exchange rates is $CN^- > I^- > Br^- > Cl^-$, which is also the order of decreasing stabilities of these complexes. Later kinetic studies have shown that the more stable $Pt[SC(NH_2)_2]_4^{2+}$ exchanges [24] much more rapidly with $^{35}SC(NH_2)_2$ than $Pt(EtNH_2)_4^{2+}$ exchanges with labeled $EtNH_2$. Also, recall that $Pt(NH_3)_4^{2+}$ does not exchange [45] with $^{15}NH_3$ over a period of 217 days. In all these cases, the relative rates are determined by the combined entering-group and *trans*-group effects; that is, $CN^- > I^- > Br^- > Cl^-$ and $SC(NH_2)_2 > EtNH_2$ or NH_3. A study by Teggins and Milburn [46] has demonstrated that $C_2O_4^{2-}$ is a poor entering group for the substrates $Pt(C_2O_4)_4^{2-}$ and *trans*-$Pt(NH_3)_2Cl_2$. A combination of low entering- and leaving-group reactivity and weak *trans*-effect explains the unusually slow exchange observed for the system $Pt(C_2O_4)_2^{2-}$—$C_2O_4^{2-}$.

The reaction of *trans*-$Pt(PEt_3)_2(H)Cl$ in D_2O to give *trans*-$Pt(PEt_3)_2$-$(D)Cl$ is strongly catalyzed [82] by $DCl(D^+, Cl^-)$. A novel substitution pathway has been suggested [82] involving both D^+ and Cl^- as entering groups to form a Pt(IV) intermediate, $Pt(PEt_3)_2(H)(D)Cl_2$, followed by loss of $H^+ + Cl^-$ to give the product. Studies of this type are important since hydride complexes are believed to be intermediates in certain homogeneous hydrogenation reactions catalyzed by transition metal complexes.[85]

2-5 SOLVENT EFFECTS

The solvent dependence of the reaction rates of Pt(II) complexes provides another test of the suggestion of associative activation involving solvent for the k_1 term in the rate law. The exchange reaction

(2-7) has been studied [38] in several different solvents. The results are

$$\text{trans-Pt(py)}_2\text{Cl}_2 + {}^{36}\text{Cl}^- \rightleftharpoons \text{trans-Pt(py)}_2{}^{36}\text{Cl}_2 + \text{Cl}^- \quad\quad (2\text{-}7)$$

summarized in Table 2-11. It was found that the k_1 term is important in solvents that are capable of good coordination with Pt(II); the order of increasing k_1 is ROH $<$ H_2O, $MeNO_2$ $<$ DMSO. In addition, a very recent study [79] gives $k_1(\text{DMSO}) \gg k_1(\text{MeOH})$ for the trans-Pt(PEt$_3$)$_2$Cl$_2$ complex. The fact that the k_1 values are larger for DMSO than for H_2O or MeOH strongly supports the interpretation of an associative mechanism involving solvent, and is inconsistent with a dissociative mechanism in which bond-breaking of the leaving group is more important than bond-making with a solvent molecule.

In solvents that are expected to be poor entering groups, the k_2 term for reaction (2-7) is more important. Solvents in this category include C_6H_6, CCl_4, $t\text{-}C_4H_9OH$, $(Me)_2CO$, and EtOAc. The rates of Pt(II) substitutions discussed in previous sections were examined in protic solvents, principally water and ethanol. Thorough studies of the k_2 path in aprotic solvents are needed, since the exact role of solvation in the ground state and in the transition state is an important unknown at the present time. In studies of substitution reactions at saturated carbon, for example, the entering-group rate order in protic solvents is $I^- > Br^- > Cl^-$, but in certain cases in acetone [76] and DMF [89] the order reverses ($Cl^- > Br^- > I^-$). In the case of trans-Pt(PEt$_3$)$_2$Cl$_2$ as substrate, Belluco and coworkers have shown [79] that the entering-group rate order of $I^- > Br^- > Cl^-$ is maintained in acetone, DMSO, and methanol, in spite of the fact that Cl^- becomes more reactive relative to I^- (by a factor of about 60) in going from methanol to acetone. These data are in Table 2-11. Similar results have been obtained by others.[77] From these initial results it is apparent that the *change* in solvation of the entering group from the ground to the transition state is of less importance than the nature of the entering group itself in determining the rates of Pt(II) substitutions, consistent with strong associative activation. The much larger importance of solvent (relative to entering group) in determining the rates of halide substitutions for certain saturated-carbon substrates indicates for these systems a model in which the mode of activation has considerably less associative character than in the Pt(II) case.

2-6   EFFECT OF CHARGE ON THE COMPLEX

Martin and co-workers have provided probably the most conclusive evidence for an associative solvent path, which is the *lack* of a large

Table 2-11   *Solvent effects in Pt(II) substitution reactions* [a]

trans-Pt(py)$_2$Cl$_2$ + R^{36}Cl $\rightleftharpoons$

$\qquad\qquad$ *trans*-Pt(py)$_2{}^{36}$Cl$_2$ + RCl

Solvents in which the reaction is independent of [R^{36}Cl]	$k_1 \times 10^5$, sec^{-1}
H$_2$O	3.5
DMSO	380
MeNO$_2$	3.2
EtOH	1.4
n-C$_3$H$_7$OH	0.42

Solvents in which the reaction depends on [R^{36}Cl]	k_2, M^{-1} sec^{-1} [b]
CCl$_4$	10^4
C$_6$H$_6$	10^2
m-cresol	10^{-1}
t-C$_4$H$_9$OH	10^{-1}
EtOAc	10^{-2}
Me$_2$CO	10^{-2}
DMF	10^{-3}

trans-Pt(PEt$_3$)$_2$Cl$_2$ + Y $\rightarrow$

$\qquad\qquad$ *trans*-Pt(PEt$_3$)$_2$(Cl)Y + Cl$^-$

$k_2 \times 10^3$, M^{-1} sec^{-1} [c]

Y	Me$_2$CO [d]	DMSO [e]	MeOH [f]
Cl$^-$	1.5	0.7	0.03
Br$^-$	16	5.8	0.93
I$^-$	230	160	263
SCN$^-$	180	246	371
SC(NH$_2$)$_2$	40,000	15,200	very large

[a] R = n-octadecylbenzyldimethylammonium; t = 25°C; from Ref. 38.

[b] The k_2 value refers to the corrected rate for free Cl$^-$ as entering group.

[c] The k_2 values are for free ions as entering groups; from Ref. 79.

[d] t = 25°C; $k_1 < 10^{-6}$ sec^{-1}.

[e] t = 25°C; $k_1 = 2 \times 10^{-5}$ sec^{-1}.

[f] t = 30°C; $k_1 = 10^{-7}$ sec^{-1}.

Table 2-12   *Effect of substrate charge on the rates of Pt(II) substitution reactions in water at 20°* [a]

Complex	$k_1(H_2O) \times 10^5$, sec^{-1}
$PtCl_4^{2-}$	3.9
$Pt(NH_3)Cl_3^-$ (*trans* Cl)	0.62
$Pt(NH_3)Cl_3^-$ (*cis* Cl)	5.6
cis-$Pt(NH_3)_2Cl_2$	2.5
trans-$Pt(NH_3)_2Cl_2$	9.8
$Pt(NH_3)_3Cl^+$	2.6

[a] Values of k_1 for the first acid hydrolyses of chloroammineplatinum(II) complexes; from Ref. 16.

rate effect in the k_1 path for reactions of complexes carrying different net charges in aqueous solution.[16, 26, 27]   The pertinent results are given in Table 2-12.   Proceeding from $Pt(NH_3)_3Cl^+$ to $PtCl_4^{2-}$, the k_1 rate stays roughly constant; this is not consistent with a dissociative (bond-breaking) mechanism, but is reasonable assuming any associative path such as the **A** mechanism shown in Figure 2-1.

There are small but significant substrate-charge effects on the k_2 term with certain entering groups.   In particular, $k_2(NO_2^-)$ is larger than $k_2(Cl^-)$ with $Pt(dien)Br^+$ as substrate, but $k_2(Cl^-)$ is larger than $k_2(NO_2^-)$ with $Pt(dien)OH_2^{2+}$ as substrate.[20]   These data are given in Table 2-13. This relative decrease in the reactivity of NO_2^- with respect to the more

Table 2-13   *Effect of the nature of the substrate on the reactivities of Cl⁻ and NO₂⁻ with Pt(II) complexes*

Complex	Conditions	$k_2 \times 10^4$, M^{-1} sec^{-1} for reaction with	
		Cl⁻	NO₂⁻
$Pt(dien)OH_2^{2+}$ [a]	aq. soln, 25°	1.0×10^4	0.56×10^4
$Pt(dien)Br^+$ [b]	aq. soln, 25°	8.8	37
trans-$Pt(pip)_2Cl_2$ [c]	MeOH soln, 30°	9.3	20
trans-$Pt(py)_2Cl_2$ [c]	MeOH soln, 30°	4.5	6.8
trans-$Pt(PEt_3)_2Cl_2$ [c]	MeOH soln, 30°	0.29	0.27

[a] From Ref. 20.
[b] From Ref. 15.
[c] From Refs. 19 and 22.

purely nucleophilic Cl^- is evidence for an electrophilic contribution
($Pt \rightarrow NO_2^- \pi$ bonding) to the NO_2^- reactivity, which would be expected
to decrease as the positive charge on the complex increases.   A related
comparison from Table 2-13 is that NO_2^- and Cl^- show different relative
reactivities toward the substrates $trans$-$Pt(pip)_2Cl_2$ and $trans$-$Pt(PEt_3)_2Cl_2$.[19]
Thus the ratio $k_2(NO_2^-)/k_2(Cl^-)$ is greater than two for the former complex and less than one for the latter.   A possible explanation for this
result is that the $d(\pi)$ electrons are less available for bonding with an incoming group in $trans$-$Pt(PEt_3)_2Cl_2$, owing to $Pt \rightarrow PEt_3 \pi$ bonding.
Thus, the effect is similar to increasing the positive charge on the complex,
adding to the evidence for a contribution of an *electrophilic* nature to the
reactivity of NO_2^- in planar substitutions.

2-7   THERMODYNAMIC PARAMETERS

Very few detailed studies of the effect of temperature on the reaction
rates have appeared for planar substitutions.   Table 2-14 summarizes
values of $\Delta H^{\ddagger}$ and $\Delta S^{\ddagger}$ for some representative reactions.   In all cases
studied the $\Delta S^{\ddagger}$ values are negative.   It is interesting that the reactions
involving the two good entering ligands, I^- and $SC(NH_2)_2$, have the
smallest $\Delta H^{\ddagger}$ values in the group.

Table 2-14   *Thermodynamic parameters for some Pt(II) substitution reactions in water solution* [a]

Complex	Entering group	$\Delta H^{\ddagger}$, kcal mole^{-1}	$\Delta S^{\ddagger}$, eu
$PtCl_4^{2-}$ [b]	H_2O	21	-8
$Pt(NH_3)Cl_3^-$ [b]	H_2O	19	-15
cis-$Pt(NH_3)_2Cl_2$ [b]	H_2O	20	-14
$trans$-$Pt(NH_3)_2Cl_2$ [b]	H_2O	20	-11
$Pt(NH_3)_3Cl^+$ [b]	H_2O	18	-18
$Pt(dien)Cl^+$ [c]	Br^-	14	-23
$Pt(dien)Cl^+$ [c]	I^-	10	-30
$Pt(dien)Cl^+$ [c]	$SC(NH_2)_2$	10	-28
$trans$-$Pt(PEt_3)_2Cl_2$ [d]	NO_2^-	15	-30
$trans$-$Pt(pip)_2Cl_2$ [d]	NO_2^-	14	-25

[a] Leaving group is Cl^-.
[b] From Ref. 16 and papers cited therein.
[c] From Ref. 87.
[d] From Ref. 64.

2-8 EVALUATION OF THE MODEL AND EVIDENCE FOR AN A PROCESS

We remark at the outset that it is now established beyond reasonable doubt that the intimate mechanism of square-planar substitutions is the **a** type; that is, the energy of the transition state is profoundly affected by the nature of the entering group. We must now take up the question of whether the square-planar Pt(II) substitutions are better designated as **A** or I_a processes. The theoretical arguments presented earlier lead to the conclusion that planar d^8 substitutions are ideal cases for an associative mechanism involving a five-coordinate intermediate; that is, the **A** process.

Careful study of the kinetic plot k_{obs} versus [Y] is needed to suggest cases where the five-coordinate intermediate of an **A** mechanism is definitely involved. Haake has reported [36] that the reaction of cis-$Pt(NH_3)_2(NO_2)Cl$ with NO_2^- in aqueous solution does not strictly obey the general rate law. This suggests that the five-coordinate intermediate $Pt(NH_3)_2(NO_2)_2Cl^-$ builds up during the course of the reaction. However, it has been shown [15] that efficient capture of the aquo-complex intermediate of the "k_1 path" by the leaving anion can cause such rate effects. The general problem of the possible accumulation of a five-coordinate intermediate desperately needs thorough study.

There is a compelling reason to believe that further kinetic investigations will establish many **A** processes in square-planar substitutions. Let us focus on an associative exchange reaction, for example, $PtI_4^{2-} + {}^*I^-$, where the plot of free energy versus reaction coordinate *must* be symmetric. As shown in Figure 2-13, there are two possibilities, depending on whether the detailed mechanism is **A** or I_a. In the **A** process, there is a minimum in the curve corresponding to a symmetrical (D_{3h}) trigonal-bipyramidal intermediate, and the two maxima represent distorted (unsymmetric) trigonal-bipyramidal structures. In the I_a process, the symmetric trigonal bipyramid is the highest-energy structure and is the transition state. However, the available evidence supports the postulate of an intermediate, since there are several stable trigonal-bipyramidal d^8 ML_5 complexes. The most important one to cite in our discussion here is $[(C_6H_5)_3PMe]_3$-$[Pt(SnCl_3)_5]$, the one example [65] of a stable trigonal-bipyramidal Pt(II) complex containing monodentate ligands (it has D_{3h} symmetry in the $PtSn_5$ part). Apparently, the strong π-acceptor nature [66] of $SnCl_3^-$ stabilizes the trigonal-bipyramidal structure, consistent with the formulation of the π-*trans* effect. It seems reasonable to assume that the process $Pt(SnCl_3)_4^{2-} + SnCl_3^- \rightarrow Pt(SnCl_3)_5^{3-}$ requires some activation energy, in which case the **A** reaction curve in Figure 2-13 is appropriate. A very worthwhile experiment would be the isolation of a compound containing square-planar $Pt(SnCl_3)_4^{2-}$, which would establish that both the square-

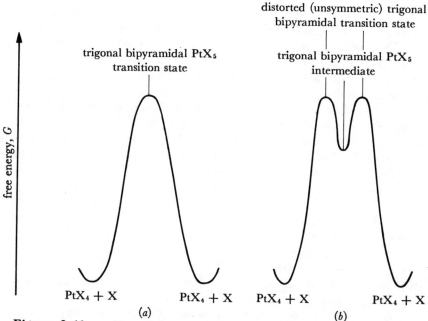

Figure 2-13 *Plots of free energy vs. reaction coordinate for the associative exchange reaction $PtX_4 + {}^*X \rightleftharpoons Pt^*X_4 + X$: (a) I_a mechanism; (b) A mechanism.*

planar and trigonal-bipyramidal structures correspond to minima in the potential-energy surface.

The validity of the A mechanism of Figure 2-1 is certainly strongly suggested by the impressive correlation of a wide variety of substituent effects based on a process that proceeds through an approximately trigonal-bipyramidal transition state and a trigonal-bipyramidal intermediate. Intimate analysis of the five-coordinate transition state shows that the three ligands that occupy the trigonal plane in the trigonal bipyramid may take advantage of certain σ- and π-bonding possibilities which are substantially changed from the ground-state square-planar complex. On the other hand, the bonding situation of the two apical ligands is not appreciably different from the ground-state complex. *Thus, the assumption of an approximately trigonal-bipyramidal geometry for the transition state correctly predicts relatively large substituent effects for the ligands in the trigonal plane (the trans, entering, and leaving groups) and relatively small effects for the apical ligands (the cis groups).*

Trans and *cis* effects alone cannot decide whether the I_a or the **A** model is more realistic for square-planar substitutions. However, a comparison of the observed entering- and leaving-group effects with the *trans* effect is entirely consistent with the existence of the five-coordinate intermediate of an **A** process. The fact that powerful *trans*-labilizing and entering groups such as I^- and CN^- are replaced much more slowly than poorer *trans* and entering groups (such as Cl^-), in $Pt(dien)X^+$ complexes, shows that in these cases the trigonal-bipyramidal transition state must necessarily be quite unsymmetric. Specifically, these experiments show that appreciable stretching of the Pt—CN bond has developed in the transition state when CN^- is a leaving group, but to understand the *trans* effect in our model, the Pt—CN bond is required to be rather firm in the transition state when CN^- is a *trans* group. In short, in comparing CN^- as a leaving group with CN^- as a *trans* group, it appears that a leaving CN^- is less firmly attached than a *trans* CN^- in the trigonal plane of the transition state. The model that best accounts for this observation is an **A** process, with two maxima and one minimum (the intermediate) in the free-energy versus reaction-coordinate profile. We emphasize that, of the two model pathways, *it is the* **A** *path alone that consistently goes through an unsymmetric trigonal-bipyramidal transition state*. We postulate here that the transition state lies before the intermediate (formation of the trigonal bipyramid is rate-determining) for substitutions in which the entering group is higher than the leaving group in the *trans*-effect series, and after the intermediate (dissociation of the trigonal bipyramid is rate-determining) if the reverse is true. The former situation is illustrated by reaction (2-8) and the latter

$$Pt(dien)Cl^+ + CN^- \rightarrow Pt(dien)CN^+ + Cl^- \qquad (2\text{-}8)$$

situation by the forward reaction (2-9). The two model free-energy

$$Pt(dien)I^+ + Cl^- \rightleftharpoons Pt(dien)Cl^+ + I^- \qquad (2\text{-}9)$$

profiles for an **A** process are shown in Figure 2-14.

In searching for kinetic evidence for a five-coordinate intermediate, one should choose the reaction direction that gives greater importance to the dissociation of the leaving group in reaching the transition state. Two reactions that are obvious candidates for detailed kinetic investigations are (2-9) and (2-10). That is, it would be instructive to examine these

$$Pt(dien)I^+ + Br^- \rightleftharpoons Pt(dien)Br^+ + I^- \qquad (2\text{-}10)$$

reactions in the direction in which it is the *dissociation* of the assumed trigonal-bipyramidal intermediate that is rate-determining.

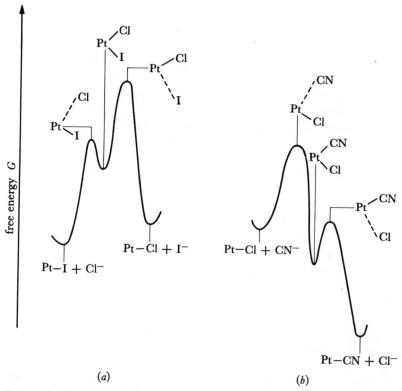

$$(a) \qquad\qquad\qquad (b)$$

Figure 2-14   *Free-energy profiles for an associative* **A** *process: (a) Suggested profile for the reaction* $Pt(dien)I^+ + Cl^- \rightleftharpoons Pt(dien)Cl^+ + I^-$. *The dien group is left out. In the forward direction, the transition state is formed after the intermediate. Considerable Pt---I bond dissociation has developed in the transition state. (b) Suggested profile for the reaction* $Pt(dien)Cl^+ + CN^- \rightleftharpoons Pt(dien)CN^+ + Cl^-$. *The dien group is left out. In the forward direction, the transition state is formed before the intermediate. Relatively very little Pt—Cl bond dissociation has developed in the transition state, although the* Cl^- *group has "moved" to allow the Pt---CN bond to develop.*

Recent evidence for an unsymmetric five-coordinate transition state comes from the observation [78] that the reactions of *trans*-Pt(pip)$_2$Cl$_2$ with NO$_2^-$ and ^{36}Cl$^-$ in methanol solution are catalyzed by nitrous acid and boric acid. In these cases there is an additional term in the rate law which has the form k_3[complex][Y][acid]. Presumably, one molecule of acid, bound in some fashion to the complex, is able to lower the energy of the transition state and promote the entry of a group Y. It should be noted that the postulated unsymmetric five-coordinate transition state in the **A** model pathway may have some free space in the "trigonal" plane between the leaving group and the *trans* group (refer to Fig. 2-14) for coordination to an additional group. Weak bonding of a π acceptor molecule such as HNO_2 or H_3BO_3 in this transition state is the suggested [78] mechanism of catalysis. The intermediate in both the catalyzed and uncatalyzed substitution reactions involving $^{36}Cl^-$ would be the symmetric trigonal-bypyramidal complex *trans*-$Pt(pip)_2Cl_3^-$.

2-9 SUMMARY OF Pt(II) SUBSTITUTION REACTIONS

The major activation process of square-planar substitution reactions is associative (**a**). The assumption of an **A** mechanism via a trigonal-bipyramidal intermediate is able to account for all the evidence available at this time. The main evidence for the associative-trigonal-bipyramidal mechanism for the k_2 path is as follows:

1. a unified interpretation of substituent effects based on the model of an **A** process;

2. the large decrease in the rate observed on blocking the attack positions. It is found that *cis* blocking is more effective than *trans* blocking;

3. the large *entering-group* effect which closely parallels the *trans*-effect order of ligands;

4. the observation that no $Pt(dien)OH^+$ is formed during the reaction of $Pt(dien)Br^+$ with Y^- in the presence of OH^-, showing that there can be no intervention of the solvent along the k_2 path.

The main evidence for the associative-trigonal-bipyramidal mechanism involving solvent as reagent in the k_1 term is as follows:

1. the large decrease in the k_1 rate on blocking the attack positions in several Pt(II) complexes;

2. the observation that the k_1 rate is relatively insensitive to changes in the net charge on the complex;

3. solvent-effect experiments that show good *coordinating* solvents enhance the k_1 term. For example, $k_1(DMSO) > k_1(H_2O)$ in reactions with PtA_2Cl_2 complexes.

2-10 OTHER CENTRAL METAL ATOMS

The substitution reactions of square-planar complexes containing central metals other than Pt(II) have been relatively little studied, but the few studies available indicate that the principal rate effects established in Pt(II) reactions also apply to other square-planar systems. Thus, we shall not discuss these cases in detail, but instead indicate some typical results.

Pd(II), Ni(II)

In general, the square-planar complexes of Pd(II) and Ni(II) are much more labile than analogous Pt(II) complexes. This is probably because Ni(II) and Pd(II) are able to add a fifth group more easily than Pt(II). Axial interactions in solution are quite common in these cases. Very few good comparisons are available, but, allowing for temperature differences in certain cases, the results given in Table 2-15 indicate that the relative reactivities of analogous Ni(II), Pd(II), Pt(II) complexes are approximately $10^{7-8}:10^{5-6}:1$. It is probable that substitutions in the square planar Ni(II) and Pd(II) complexes proceed by an **A** mechanism, considering the numerous examples [75] of stable five-coordinate complexes containing these central metals.

A particularly interesting rate study [86] is of the sterically hindered complex $Pd(Et_4dien)Cl^+$. It has been found that $Pd(Et_4dien)Cl^+$ has a reactivity pattern in aqueous solution that is the same in gross features as the reactivity pattern of typical six-coordinate Co(III) complexes. Thus $Pd(Et_4dien)Cl^+$ reacts with Br^- and I^- at a rate independent of the concentration of the entering group. The only reasonable conclusion is that

Table 2-15   *Rates of reaction of analogous Pt(II), Pd(II), and Ni(II) complexes at 25° [a]*

Complex	[py], M	Solvent	k_{obs}, sec^{-1}
Pt(dien)SCN^{+} [b]	0.00090	H_2O	6.2×10^{-8}
Pd(dien)SCN^{+} [b]	0.00123	H_2O	4.2×10^{-2}
Pt(dien)NO$_2^{+}$ [b]	0.00592	H_2O	5.0×10^{-8}
Pd(dien)NO$_2^{+}$ [b]	0.00124	H_2O	3.3×10^{-2}
Pt(Et$_4$dien)Cl^{+}	0.001	H_2O	8.6×10^{-6} [c]
Pd(Et$_4$dien)Cl^{+} [d]	0.001	H_2O	2.0×10^{-3}
trans-Pt(PEt$_3$)$_2$(o-tolyl)Cl [e]	0.0062	EtOH	1.7×10^{-5}
trans-Pd(PEt$_3$)$_2$(o-tolyl)Cl	0.0062	EtOH	5.8×10^{-3} [f]
trans-Ni(PEt$_3$)$_2$(o-tolyl)Cl	0.0062	EtOH	1.6×10^{-2} [g]

[a] Pyridine as entering group.
[b] From Ref. 34.
[c] Rate at 80°; from Ref. 62.
[d] From Ref. 86.
[e] From Ref. 17.
[f] Rate at −40°; from Ref. 17.
[g] Rate at −65°; from Ref. 17.

an associative pathway is not available and a mechanism involving dissociative activation is operative. The rate of the base-hydrolysis reaction of Pd(Et$_4$dien)Cl$^+$ *depends* on the concentration of OH$^-$. Since the usual associative solvolysis pathway is presumably not available for reaction of Pd(Et$_4$dien)Cl$^+$ with OH$^-$, it chooses instead the conjugate-base-type mechanism common in octahedral substitutions (see Chapter 3). Strong evidence in support of this conclusion is the fact that Pd(MeEt$_4$dien)Cl$^+$,

which has a central $\diagdown$ N—Me group instead of a central $\diagdown$ N—H group, $\diagup$ $\diagup$

reacts with OH$^-$ at a rate independent of [OH$^-$].

A study of the entering-group effect in Pd(II) substitutions has been carried out [67] for the substrate Pd(acac)$_2$ in aqueous solution. Although the detailed mechanism is fairly complicated, the relative reactivities of different entering groups decrease in the order SCN$^-$ > I$^-$ > Br$^-$ > Cl$^-$ > H$_2$O, OH$^-$. This is the same order as for Pt(II) substitutions.

Rate studies with OH$^-$ as entering group and Pd(dien)I$^+$ and Pd(dien)SCN$^+$ as substrates have been completed.[68] In both cases, the rates are independent of [OH$^-$]. It appears well-established from these studies that OH$^-$ is a poor entering group for direct substitution in Pd(II), as is the case for Pt(II). The earlier rate studies [69] that suggest OH$^-$ is a good entering group in Pd(II) substitutions should be investigated again.

In addition to the limited rate data available [17] for Ni(PR$_3$)$_2$(R)X substrates, the reaction rates of amineoximatonickel(II) complexes with EDTA have been investigated.[21] Numerous substances catalyze the reaction, such as NH$_3$ and C$_2$O$_4^{2-}$. The reactions follow the general two-term rate law. Similar two-term kinetic behavior in the reactions of EDTA with Ni(cysteine)$_2^{2-}$ and Ni(cysteine-methyl-ester)$_2$ has been taken as evidence of a square-planar structure, with bidentate S,N-donor cysteine, for these substrates.[88]

Au(III)

The two-term rate law, now well-established in square-planar substitution reactions, was first discovered for reaction [70] (2-11) in aqueous solution.

$$AuCl_4^- + {}^{36}Cl^- \rightleftharpoons Au^{36}Cl_4^- + Cl^- \qquad (2\text{-}11)$$

Both the k_1 and k_2 values for reaction (2-11) are substantially larger than those for the ^{36}Cl$^-$ exchange with PtCl$_4^{2-}$, suggesting an **a** mechanism with increased bonding to the entering group in the transition state in the Au(III) system. As in the case of Pt(II) substitutions, solvent water is the initial entering group for the k_1 pathway.[70, 84] The reactions of Au(dien)X^{2+} complexes with Y ligands follow the two-term rate law and are faster than the analogous reactions involving Pt(dien)X^+, consistent with an associative mechanism.[63]   For example, k_2 for the reaction of Au-(dien)Cl^{2+} with Br^- is 10^4 larger than k_2 for the Br^- reaction with Pt(dien)Cl^+.   In the reactions of analogous Pt(II) and Au(III) complexes with various entering groups, it appears that bond making is of more importance in the Au(III) systems, which carry one more unit of positive charge.   Finally, it is observed that the *relative* reactivities of both X and Y in the Au(III) complexes are approximately the same as the relative reactivities in Pt(II) complexes.[63]

Cattalini has studied [80] the reaction of $AuXCl_3$ with Y^-, where X is a neutral leaving group in the pyridine family.   The reaction follows the two-term rate law, with the entering-group order $N_3^- > NO_2^- > Cl^-$. The fact that a ligand such as pyridine is displaced before Cl^- in $AuXCl_3$ is very interesting and deserves further study.   Recall that in Pt(py)$_2Cl_2$ it is always a Cl^- that is displaced most readily by an entering group Y.[22]

Rh(I), Ir(I)

The few data available for reactions of planar Rh(I) and Ir(I) complexes indicate that they react by an associative process.   For example, the complexes Rh(CO)$_2$(p-anisidine)Cl and Ir(CO)$_2$(p-toluidine)Cl undergo second-order exchange with ^{14}CO at $-80°$ in ethanol, with $k_2 = 2$ M^{-1} sec^{-1} for both systems.[71]   It is quite probable that these are **A** processes with unusually stable five-coordinate intermediates, because the related five-coordinate complexes Ir(P(C_6H_5)$_3$)$_2$(CO)$_2$Cl [72] and Ir(P-(C_6H_5)$_3$)$_3$(CO)H [73] have been isolated.

The substitution of C_2D_4 for C_2H_4 in Rh(C_2H_4)$_2$(acac) is extremely rapid at 25°, whereas C_2D_4 does not substitute for C_2H_4 in (π-C_5H_5)-Rh(C_2H_4)$_2$ during a period of five hours at 100°.[74]   Apparently, an associative pathway exists for Rh(C_2H_4)$_2$(acac) but not for (π-C_5H_5)-Rh(C_2H_4)$_2$.   The Rh $5p_z$ orbital may not be available in (π-C_5H_5)-Rh(C_2H_4)$_2$, although the rapid ^{14}CO exchange in (π-C_5H_5)Rh(CO)$_2$ indicates a steric factor may be more important in the former case.

REFERENCES

1. H. B. Gray, *Progr. Transition Metal Chem.*, **1**, 239 (1965).
2. H. B. Gray and C. J. Ballhausen, *J. Am. Chem. Soc.*, **85**, 260 (1963).
3. C. K. Jørgensen, *Absorption Spectra and Chemical Bonding in Complexes*, Addison-Wesley, Reading, Mass., 1962, p. 157.
4. J. Chatt, G. A. Gamlen, and L. E. Orgel, *J. Chem. Soc.*, **1958**, 486.
5. G. Maki, *J. Chem. Phys.*, **28**, 651 (1958); **29**, 162, 1129 (1958).
6. C. J. Ballhausen and A. D. Liehr, *J. Am. Chem. Soc.*, **81**, 538 (1959).
7. M. I. Ban, *Acta Chim. Acad. Sci. Hung.*, **19**, 459 (1959).
8. S. Kida, J. Fukita, K. Nakamoto, and R. Tsuchida, *Bull. Chem. Soc.* (*Japan*), **31**, 79 (1958).

9. R. F. Fenske, D. S. Martin, Jr., and K. Ruedenberg, *Inorg. Chem.*, **1**, 441 (1962).
10. J. R. Perumareddi, A. D. Liehr, and A. W. Adamson, *J. Am. Chem. Soc.*, **85**, 249 (1963).
11. C. J. Ballhausen, N. Bjerrum, R. Dingle, K. Eriks, and C. R. Hare, *Inorg. Chem.*, **4**, 445 (1965).
12. D. S. Martin, Jr., and C. A. Lenhardt, *Inorg. Chem.*, **3**, 1368 (1964); P. Day, A. F. Orchard, A. J. Thomson, and R. J. P. Williams, *J. Chem. Phys.*, **42**, 1973 (1965); S. I. Shupack, E. Billig, R. J. H. Clark, R. Williams, and H. B. Gray, *J. Am. Chem. Soc.*, **86**, 4594 (1964).
13. D. S. Martin, Jr., M. A. Tucker, and A. J. Kassman, *Inorg. Chem.*, **4**, 1682 (1965).
14. F. Basolo and R. G. Pearson, *Mechanisms of Inorganic Reactions*, Wiley, New York, 1958, Chap. 4.
15. H. B. Gray, *J. Am. Chem. Soc.*, **84**, 1548 (1962).
16. M. A. Tucker, C. B. Colvin, and D. S. Martin, Jr., *Inorg. Chem.*, **3**, 1373 (1964).
17. F. Basolo, J. Chatt, H. B. Gray, R. G. Pearson, and B. L. Shaw, *J. Chem. Soc.*, **1961**, 2207.
18. F. Basolo and R. G. Pearson, in *Progress in Inorganic Chemistry* (F. A. Cotton, ed.), Wiley-Interscience, New York, 1962, Vol. 4.
19. U. Belluco, L. Cattalini, and A. Turco, *J. Am. Chem. Soc.*, **86**, 226, 3257 (1964).
20. H. B. Gray and R. J. Olcott, *Inorg. Chem.*, **1**, 481 (1962).
21. R. K. Murmann, *Inorg. Chem.*, **2**, 116 (1963); D. L. Lewis and R. K. Murmann, *J. Inorg. Nucl. Chem.*, **25**, 1431 (1963).
22. U. Belluco, L. Cattalini, F. Basolo, R. G. Pearson, and A. Turco, *J. Am. Chem. Soc.*, **87**, 241 (1965).
23. A. A. Grinberg and L. E. Nikol'skaya, *Zh. Prikl. Khim.*, **22**, 542 (1949).
24. A. A. Grinberg and S. S. Borzakoya, *Zh. Neorgan. Khim.*, **2**, 2368 (1957).
25. A. A. Grinberg and E. N. In'kova, *Zh. Neorgan. Khim.*, **3**, 1315 (1958).
26. L. F. Grantham, T. S. Elleman, and D. S. Martin, Jr., *J. Am. Chem. Soc.*, **77**, 2965 (1955).
27. T. S. Elleman, J. W. Reishus, and D. S. Martin, Jr., *J. Am. Chem. Soc.*, **81**, 10 (1959).
28. A. A. Grinberg, L. E. Nikol'skaya, and G. A. Shagisultanova, *Dokl. Akad. Nauk SSSR*, **101**, 1059 (1955).
29. O. E. Zvyagintsev and E. F. Karandashova, *Dokl. Akad. Nauk SSSR*, **101**, 93 (1955).
30. O. E. Zvyagintsev and E. F. Shubochkina, *Zh. Neorgan. Khim.*, **3**, 1139 (1958).
31. A. A. Grinberg and Y. N. Kukushkin, *Russ. J. Inorg. Chem.*, **4**, 139 (1959).
32. A. A. Grinberg, *Russ. J. Inorg. Chem.*, **4**, 683 (1959).
33. D. Banerjea, F. Basolo, and R. G. Pearson, *J. Am. Chem. Soc.*, **79**, 4055 (1957).
34. F. Basolo, H. B. Gray, and R. G. Pearson, *J. Am. Chem. Soc.*, **82**, 4200 (1960).
35. A. A. Grinberg and L. E. Nikol'skaya, *Zh. Prikl. Khim.*, **24**, 893 (1951).
36. P. Haake, *Proc. Chem. Soc.*, **1962**, 278.
37. P. Haake and P. A. Cronin, *Inorg. Chem.*, **2**, 879 (1963).
38. R. G. Pearson, H. B. Gray, and F. Basolo, *J. Am. Chem. Soc.*, **82**, 787 (1960).
39. H. B. Gray and R. Price, unpublished results, 1962.

40. A. V. Babaeva and R. I. Rudyi, *Zh. Neorgan. Khim.*, **6**, 2457 (1961).
41. A. A. Grinberg and M. A. Kuz'mina, *Dokl. Akad. Nauk SSSR*, **144,** 798 (1962).
42. A. A. Grinberg and G. A. Shagisul anova, *Radiokhimiya*, **2**, 574 (1960); A. A. Grinberg and L. E. Nikol'skaya, *Radiokhimiya*, **2**, 584 (1960).
43. B. I. Peshchevitskii, V. P. Kazakov, and V. M. Shul'man, *Izv. Sibirsk. Otd. Akad. Nauk SSSR, Ser. Khim. Nauk*, **1963** (1), 65; B. I. Peshchevitskii and V. P. Kazakov, *Zh. Neorgan. Khim.*, **8**, 250 (1963); *Izv. Sibirsk. Otd. Akad. Nauk SSSR, Ser. Khim. Nauk*, **1963** (2), 20.
44. I. B. Beisuker, *Zh. Strukt. Khim.*, **4**, 461 (1963).
45. D. R. Llewellyn, C. J. O'Connor, and A. C. Odell, *J. Chem. Soc.*, **1964**, 196.
46. J. E. Teggins and R. M. Milburn, *Inorg. Chem.*, **3**, 364 (1964).
47. U. Belluco, L. Cattalini, and A. Orio, *Gazz. Chem. Ital.*, **93**, 1422 (1963); U. Belluco, R. Ettorre, and M. Mortelli, *Gazz. Chem. Ital.*, **94**, 356 (1964); U. Belluco, L. Cattalini, M. Mortelli, and R. Ettorre, *Gazz. Chem. Ital.*, **94,**, 733 (1964); L. Cattalini, U. Belluco, M. Mortelli, and R. Ettorre, *Gazz. Chem. Ital.*, **95**, 567 (1965); U. Belluco, L. Cattalini, M. Graziani, and M. Mortelli; *Gazz. Chem. Ital.*, **95**, 576 (1965).
48. A. Werner, *Z. Anorg. Allgem. Chem.*, **3**, 267 (1893).
49. I. I. Chernyaev, *Ann. Inst. Platine* (*USSR*), **4**, 261 (1926); I. I. Chernyaev, *Izv. Sektora Platiny i Drug. Blagorodn. Metal. Inst. Obshch. i Neorgan. Khim. Acad. Nauk SSSR*, **5**, 118 (1927).
50. Z. Simon and M. Brezeener, *Rev. Roumaine Chim.*, **9**, 113 (1964); *Studii Cercetari Chim.*, **12**, 107 (1964).
51. F. Basolo, *Proc. ACS Conf. Mechanisms Inorganic Reactions*, University of Kansas, 1964.
52. A. A. Grinberg, *Ann. Inst. Platine* (*USSR*), **5**, 109 (1927).
53. B. V. Nekrasov, *Kurs Obshchei Khimii*, Moscow-Leningrad, 1935, p. 77.
54. Y. K. Syrkin, *Izv. Akad. Nauk SSSR Otd. Khim. Nauk*, **1948**, 69.
55. S. S. Batsanov, *Russ. J. Inorg. Chem.*, **4**, 773 (1959).
56. H. M. E. Cardwell, *Chem. & Ind.* (*London*), **1955**, 422.
57. J. Chatt, L. A. Duncanson, and L. M. Venanzi, *Chem. & Ind.* (*London*), **1955**, 749.
58. J. Chatt, L. A. Duncanson, and L. M. Venanzi, *J. Chem. Soc.*, **1955**, 4456.
59. L. E. Orgel, *J. Inorg. Nucl. Chem.*, **2**, 137 (1956).
60. R. G. Pearson, *J. Phys. Chem.*, **63**, 321 (1959).
61. G. W. Parshall, *J. Am. Chem. Soc.*, **86**, 5367 (1964).
62. R. Wanguo, Masters thesis, Northwestern University, 1965.
63. W. H. Baddley and F. Basolo, *Inorg. Chem.*, **3**, 1087 (1964).
64. A. Turco, unpublished results; quoted in Ref. 51.
65. R. D. Cramer, R. V. Lindsey, C. T. Prewitt, and U. G. Stolberg, *J. Am. Chem. Soc.*, **87**, 658 (1965).
66. R. V. Lindsey, G. W. Parshall, and U. G. Stolberg, *J. Am. Chem. Soc.*, **87**, 658 (1965).
67. R. G. Pearson and D. A. Johnson, *J. Am. Chem. Soc.*, **86**, 3983 (1964).
68. H. B. Gray and M. Drickman, unpublished results, 1963.
69. D. Banerjea and K. K. Tripathi, *J. Inorg. Nucl. Chem.*, **7**, 78 (1958).
70. R. L. Rich and H. Taube, *J. Phys. Chem.*, **58**, 1 (1954).

71. A. Wojcicki and H. B. Gray, *Proc. Chem. Soc.*, **1960**, 358; Abstr., 141st National Meeting, American Chemical Society, Washington, D.C., March, 1962, p. 32-M.
72. M. Angaletta, *Gazz. Chim. Ital.*, **89**, 2359 (1959); **90**, 1021 (1960).
73. S. S. Bath and L. Vaska, *J. Am. Chem. Soc.*, **85**, 3500 (1963).
74. R. Cramer, *J. Am. Chem. Soc.*, **86**, 217 (1964).
75. See, for example: E. L. Muetterties and R. A. Schunn, *Quart. Rev.*, to be published; J. A. Ibers, *Ann. Rev. Phys. Chem.*, **16**, 380 (1965); G. S. Benner, W. E. Hatfield, and D. W. Meek, *Inorg. Chem.*, **3**, 1544 (1964); G. Dyer, J. G. Hartley, and L. M. Venanzi, *J. Chem. Soc.*, **1965**, 1293; G. Dyer and L. M. Venanzi, *J. Chem. Soc.*, **1965**, 2771; A. D. Westland, *J. Chem. Soc.*, **1965**, 3060; L. M. Venanzi, *Angew. Chem. Intern. Ed. Engl.* **3**, 453 (1964); F. G. Mann, *Chem. & Ind. (London)* **1965**, 944.
76. S. Winstein, L. G. Savedoff, S. Smith, I. D. R. Stevens, and J. S. Gall, *Tetrahedron Letters*, **9**, 24 (1960).
77. G. Faraone, L. Cattalini, V. Ricevuto, R. Romeo, and M. Martelli, *Ann. Chim. (Rome)*, **55**, 506 (1965).
78. U. Belluco, L. Cattalini, F. Basolo, R. G. Pearson, and A. Turco, *Inorg. Chem.*, **4**, 925 (1965).
79. U. Belluco, *Proc. Conf. Mechanistic and Structural Aspects of Coordination Chemistry*, Bressanone, Italy, 1965; U. Belluco, M. Martelli, and A. Orio, *Inorg. Chem.*, in press.
80. L. Cattalini, *Proc. Conf. Mechanistic and Structural Aspects of Coordination Chemistry*, Bressanone, Italy, 1965.
81. C. D. Falk and J. Halpern, *J. Am. Chem. Soc.*, **87**, 3003 (1965).
82. C. D. Falk and J. Halpern, to be published.
83. R. Cramer, *Inorg. Chem.*, **4**, 445 (1965).
84. F. H. Fry, Ph.D. thesis, Princeton University, 1964.
85. J. Halpern, *Proc. Third Intern. Congr. Catalysis*, North-Holland, Amsterdam, 1965, pp. 146–162.
86. W. H. Baddley and F. Basolo, *J. Am. Chem. Soc.*, **86**, 2075 (1964).
87. W. H. Baddley, unpublished results; quoted in Ref. 51.
88. R. A. Libby and D. W. Margerum, *Biochemistry*, **4**, 619 (1965).
89. W. M. Weaver and J. D. Hutchison, *J. Am. Chem. Soc.*, **86**, 261 (1964).

<table>
<tr><td>chapter
three</td><td># Octahedral

Substitutions</td></tr>
</table>

Octahedral complexes, that is, complexes with six ligands disposed at the corners of a figure approximating an octahedron, are probably the most common in the literature of coordination chemistry. The scope of this chapter is thus very broad and includes a variety of electronic arrangements. But two factors are common to all octahedral systems that point to differences between their reactions and those of the square-planar systems. First, a steric factor has been introduced. The two open faces of the square complex have been filled by the fifth and sixth ligands. Thus, for comparable ligands, octahedral complexes should be more crowded and ligand-ligand repulsions should be larger. Second, octahedral complexes are not unsaturated in their σ-bonding systems. The p_z orbital that is available for involvement in σ bonding during the reactions of d^8 square-planar complexes is already so employed in the octahedral ground state. Theoretically, we predict at least reduced availability of **a** pathways in octahedral substitution. Both factors (perhaps especially the steric factor) suggest advantages for **d** processes.

Fine mechanistic distinctions, such as those between the I_d and **D** paths, can be made only on the basis of extensive data. The lone family of octahedral complexes for which adequate data are now available is the Co(III) family, notably the substituted cobalt-amine systems. These will form the subject of the bulk of this chapter. A short section compares the behavior of Cr(III) and Rh(III) complexes to Co(III) complexes, and a final section discusses other metals.

3-1 COBALT(III)

The detailed information available on Co(III) complex reactions is in large part the result of the synthetic research by the founders of coordina-

tion chemistry.   The preparative directions of Werner and Jørgensen are
still the starting point of most efforts in this field.   Of course, the modern
kineticist is interested in the very property of the Co(III) systems that
made them convenient examples for the development of structural theory.
They are relatively inert; they react at conveniently measurable rates.

The existence of many substituted Co(III)-amine complexes means
that a given reaction may be studied over a considerable range of similar
complexes, and the kinetic effects of appropriately small structure variations may be isolated.   This is the best circumstance for development of
a detailed picture of a transition state.   To interpret the effects of structure variation, detailed steric and electronic theories applicable to Co(III)
systems must be developed.   Whenever possible, these will be correlated
with available theories of the equilibrium and spectroscopic properties of
the complexes.

3-2   RATE LAWS AND RELATED MATTERS

Examples of especially careful kinetic studies of substitution reactions
of Co(III) complexes in aqueous solution include the reactions [1] of azide
and thiocyanate with $Co(en)_2(NO_2)Cl^+$, the reactions [2] of thiocyanate with
$Co(NH_3)_5NO_3^{2+}$ and $Co(NH_3)_5Br^{2+}$, the exchange [3] of labeled thiocyanate with $Co(en)_2(NCS)_2^+$, and the exchange [4] of labeled chloride
with $cis\text{-}Co(en)_2Cl_2^+$.   All the reactions were found to be first order in the
complex concentration and zero order in the entering ligand.   Analogous
studies of the reactions of these complexes with water in acid solution show
that the reactions proceed in *two* steps.   First, the original anionic ligand
is replaced by a water molecule; then, in a second step, the water molecule
is replaced by the entering anionic ligand.   The first step is rate-determining.   The entering anion is involved in the rate law for only the second
step (if outer-sphere ion association is ignored).[3]   As a result, the only
reactions for which rate constants have been obtained in acidic aqueous
solutions are the *acid hydrolysis* reaction [see Eq. (3-1)] and the *anation* reaction [see Eq. (3-2)].   In no case has the rate constant for direct replace-

$$Co(NH_3)_5X^{2+} + H_2O \rightarrow Co(NH_3)_5OH_2^{3+} + X^- \qquad (3\text{-}1)$$
$$Co(NH_3)_5OH_2^{3+} + X^- \rightarrow Co(NH_3)_5X^{2+} + H_2O \qquad (3\text{-}2)$$

ment of one anionic ligand by another been obtained.   The reaction
exemplified by Eq. (3-1) is called an acid hydrolysis because, at pH
greater than about 5, another reaction in which the entering group does
appear in the rate law becomes important.   This is the *base hydrolysis*
reaction, exemplified by Eq. (3-3).   Base hydrolysis is commonly second

$$Co(NH_3)_5X^{2+} + OH^- \rightarrow Co(NH_3)_5OH^{2+} + X^- \qquad (3\text{-}3)$$

order, first order with respect to the complex and first order in hydroxide ion. These three reactions have in common the property that an important participant in the reaction is a *solvent molecule* or its *lyate ion*. There is little reason to expect that any significant number of reactions of cobalt-ammine complexes remain to be discovered which will require mechanistic concepts beyond those needed for reactions (3-1), (3-2), and (3-3).

The fact that rate studies are possible only for reactions involving elements of the solvent is a serious limitation on the utility of rate laws. The first-order rate law for acid hydrolysis may signify only that water is present in near constant concentration. It does not reveal the role of water in the rate-determining step. In the anation reaction, kinetic dependence on the entering anion has been explained in three (different) ways.[5] The simplest is the assumption of nucleophilic attack by the anion and an I_a mechanism, but the **D** process shown in Eq. (3-4) also explains the observa-

$$Co(NH_3)_5OH_2^{3+} \underset{k_{-1}}{\overset{k_1}{\rightleftharpoons}} Co(NH_3)_5^{3+} + H_2O$$

$$Co(NH_3)_5^{3+} + X^- \overset{k_2}{\to} Co(NH_3)_5X^{2+}$$

(3-4)

tions. The dependence on the anion can arise from competition for the five-coordinate intermediate between the anion and a water molecule. If the water molecule captures the intermediate, there is no net reaction. Thus the anation rate depends on the competition governed by the relative values of k_{-1} and $k_2(X^-)$. A final suggestion attributes the dependence on the anion to a pre-equilibrium step, formation of an outer-sphere complex. If the rate-controlling process is entry of the anion from the outer sphere by any mechanism, the rate will be proportional to the concentration of the outer-sphere complex, a quantity dependent upon the anion concentration. This path is illustrated in Eq. (3-5). Finally, the rate

$$Co(NH_3)_5OH_2^{3+} + X^- \rightleftharpoons Co(NH_3)_5OH_2^{3+} \cdots X^-$$

$$Co(NH_3)_5OH_2^{3+} \cdots X^- \overset{slow}{\longrightarrow} Co(NH_3)_5X^{2+} \cdots OH_2$$

(3-5)

law for the base hydrolysis process is ambiguous as a result of possible acid-base processes involving protons on the amine ligands. (A full analysis appears in Section 3-6 on base hydrolysis.) None of the three reactions allows a simple deduction of stoichiometric mechanism from rate law.

If circumstances are favorable, there is a chance that the rate law for the acid hydrolysis reaction will not follow simple first-order form in the event that the mechanism is **D**. The analog of Eq. (3-4) may be written for **D** hydrolysis [Eq. (3-6)] and this leads to the general rate law (3-7) on application of the steady-state hypothesis. When the anion concentration is sufficiently small, this rate law reduces to the first-order form, but if k_{-1} is sufficiently large, deviation from first order will be observed as the reaction progresses. When this deviation is small, it is sometimes possible to study the hydrolysis rate as a function of added concentrations of the leaving group and to detect retardation of the hydrolysis as predicted by Eq. (3-7). Retardation by the leaving ligand, called *mass-law retardation*, is a characteristic of the **D** mechanism, but it is sometimes difficult to observe. Several organic chemical cases, thought to be **D**, show a confusing opposition between mass-law retardation and nonspecific salt effects.[6] Possible examples of mass-law retardation in octahedral substitution are discussed later. Only one is well-documented. The general problem of an ambiguous rate law remains.

$$\text{Co(NH}_3)_5\text{X}^{2+} \underset{k_{-1}}{\overset{k_1}{\rightleftharpoons}} \text{Co(NH}_3)_5^{3+} + \text{X}^- \qquad (3\text{-}6)$$

$$\text{Co(NH}_3)_5^{3+} + \text{H}_2\text{O} \overset{k_2}{\rightarrow} \text{Co(NH}_3)_5\text{OH}_2^{3+}$$

$$\frac{-d[\text{Co(NH}_3)_5\text{X}]}{dt} = \frac{k_1[\text{Co(NH}_3)_5\text{X}^{2+}])}{1 + (k_{-1}[\text{X}^-]/k_2)} \qquad (3\text{-}7)$$

If it is true that the ubiquitous participation of elements of the solvent reduces the discriminative power of rate laws and complicates attempts to classify reactions according to stoichiometric mechanism, it is equally true that ubiquitous participation of water carries important implications for the assignment of an *intimate* mechanism and analysis of the transition state. We may compare the **a** reactions of square-planar Pt(II), tetrahedral carbon, and tetrahedral phosphorus to the acid hydrolysis reactions of octahedral Co(III). In the established cases of reagent attack, there is no parallel to the unique position of water in cobalt substitutions. Attacking reagents that react 10^6 times faster than water, or even more, are known. Obviously, they appear in the rate laws when present at very low concentration. In the cobalt case no other reagent successfully competes with water. Only two possible hypotheses would leave open the possibility that Co(III) acid hydrolysis is an **a** reaction. Either water is the best reagent for attack at Co(III) or a complete lack of differences in reactivity allows water to predominate because of its concentration advantage. The first possibility is unattractive because it is difficult to reconcile with the now fairly successful theory of nucleophilicity.[7] There is nothing unusual about the water molecule either with respect to basicity, polarizability, or other measures of electron-donor ability. Adoption of the second possibility is equally unattractive, since there is no evidence in the equilibrium chemistry of Co(III) complexes to suggest that the metal is *indiscriminate* in its bonding capacity. Therefore, the simplest account of the absence of direct substitution into Co(III) complexes rests on the assumption that the entering group is at most *very weakly bound* in the transition state and does not make a significant contribution to the activation energy. Such a transition state is expected on **d** substitution paths. *In fact, we have here repeated the defining criteria of **d** activation processes.*

The hypothesis of **d** activation may be tested for its capacity to explain rate dependence on steric effects, charge-type effect, isotope effects, effects of the change of the leaving group, and the electronic effects of nonlabile substituent ligands introduced into the complexes. Following sections of this chapter indicate that the hypothesis is confirmed for at least a limited group of reactants in studies of each of these effects.

In the context of our hypothesis, we repeat that a persistent undercurrent in the discussion of ligand substitution in Co(III)-ammine complexes has divided authors into a camp which holds that it is possible to generalize about the mechanisms and a camp which holds that each case must be considered unique. There is merit in both points of view, and maintenance of a strict distinction between *intimate* and *stoichiometric* mechanism helps to clarify the issue. The hypothesis of **d** activation is capable of explaining a very large body of data and warrants provisional acceptance as a generalization. Conversely, there are few cases for which a definite distinction between I_d and **D** paths can be made. The present evidence suggests a shift from one to the other as a function of fairly small structural or environmental differences. Tests of stoichiometric mechanism are urgently needed.

3-3 STERIC EFFECTS IN Co(III) REACTIONS

Of the variety of experimental studies of the effects of structure variation on the acid hydrolysis rate, perhaps the most simply interpretable are those designed to alter steric effects. If crowding at the reaction site is increased, rates of **a** processes should be significantly reduced. Conversely, **d** processes may be accelerated, since loose bonding in the transition state allows other groups room to move to relieve strain.

An important study of steric effects in reactions of the series of complexes *trans*-Co(AA)$_2$Cl$_2^+$ (AA = a bidentate ligand derived from ethylenediamine) was carried out by Pearson et al.[8] Table 3-1 contains a summary of their results for replacement of the first chloride by water.

These results are easily understood on the basis of a **d** mechanism. The only defense left to a proponent of an **a** process is to assign the rate variation to some electronic effect that dominates steric effects. This

Table 3-1   *Rates of first acid hydrolysis of*
trans-Co(AA)$_2$Cl$_2^+$ at 25°C

AA	$k \times 10^4$, sec^{-1}
H$_2$N—CH$_2$CH$_2$—NH$_2$ (en)	0.32
H$_2$N—CH$_2$—CH(CH$_3$)—NH$_2$ (pn)	0.62
d,l-H$_2$N—CH(CH$_3$)—CH(CH$_3$)—NH$_2$ (*d,l*-bn)	1.5
meso-H$_2$N—CH(CH$_3$)—CH(CH$_3$)—NH$_2$ (*meso*-bn)	42
H$_2$N—C(CH$_3$)$_2$—C(CH$_3$)$_2$—NH$_2$ (tetrameen)	330

must be done in the face of strong evidence for their steric origin afforded by the comparison between *meso-* and *d,l*-butylenediamine. These ligands must be very similar in electronic properties, but inspection of models reveals that the methyl groups of *d,l*-butylenediamine are on opposite sides of the chelate ring from each other, whereas the methyl groups of the *meso* form are *cis* and very nearly maximally opposed. Further study of the diamine chelates shows that an even greater acceleration ($\times 10^3$) is associated with enlarging the ring from five to six members by inserting another —CH$_2$— group. Unfavorable bond angles appear to be forced on the six-membered ring. It is reasonable to assume that the ring may distort favorably in a less-crowded transition state.

3-4 THE ROLE OF THE LEAVING GROUP

If activation is not assisted by the entering group, the transition state probably lies at a point along the reaction coordinate corresponding to very weak bonding to the leaving group. This is because the main obstacle to reaction *without* the assistance of bond formation is the energy of the bond to the leaving group. When bonding to the leaving group is weak, the free energy of the transition state will be insensitive to the nature of the leaving group (except insofar as solvation is important).

The *activation free energy* is, of course, the difference between the free energy of the transition state and the free energy of the ground state. The argument above implies that this quantity should respond to changes in the leaving group in much the same way as the free energy difference between reactants and *products*, since the leaving group in the products is free (and solvated). A linear free-energy relationship is suggested between the activation energy $\Delta G^{\ddagger}$ and the standard free energy of the reaction $\Delta G°$ of the form $\Delta\Delta G^{\ddagger} = \beta\Delta\Delta G°$, where $\Delta\Delta G$ denotes the change in the free energy quantity with change in the leaving group. Moreover, β

should be close to 1.0 if activation is **d**. A more formal development of this conclusion is given by Leffler and Grunwald,[9] who show that a linear free-energy relation between rate and equilibrium energies implies a transition state resembling the reactants if β is near 0 and a transition state resembling the products if β is near 1.0. If the structure variation for which the relation is constructed is a leaving-group variation, resemblance to the products corresponds to weak bonding in the transition state.

Adequate equilibrium and rate data are available for the acid hydrolysis reactions of a series $Co(NH_3)_5X^{2+}$ to test the idea of a linear relation [10] between log k (k = acid hydrolysis rate constant at 25°C) and log K (K = acid hydrolysis equilibrium constant at 25°C; recall that log k is proportional to $\Delta G^{\ddagger}$ and log K is proportional to $\Delta G°$). Figure 3-1 shows such a plot, using data from Refs. 11, 12, and 13. For this series of similar complexes, $\beta = 1.0$, suggesting very weak bonding of the leaving group in the transition state. Further *qualitative* observations are consistent. The stable complexes $Co(NH_3)_5NCS^{2+}$ and $Co(NH_3)_5NO_2^{2+}$ undergo acid hydrolysis very slowly. A general impression of a parallel between acid hydrolysis rates and equilibria may be gained from inspection of data on diacido-bis-(ethylenediamine)Co(III) systems and $Co(CN)_5X^{3-}$ systems, although the available information is insufficient for quantitative

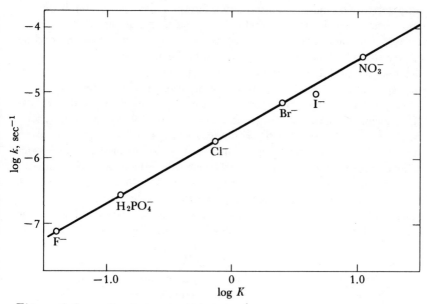

Figure 3-1 *Correlation of acid hydrolysis rates with acid hydrolysis equilibria in the system $Co(NH_3)_5X^{2+}$ at 25°C.*

treatment. One final indication of the connection between thermo-dynamic stability and the acid hydrolysis rate appears in the data developed by Yatsimirskii and Pankova [14] on standard heats of formation of $Co(NH_3)_5X^{2+}$ and $Co(en)_2X_2^+$ ions. There is a general parallel between bond energies indicated by indirectly calculated standard *gas phase* heats of formation and rates of leaving-group departure. The "stability" order given by Yatsimirskii for $Co(NH_3)_5X^{2+}$ compounds is $NO_2^- > NCS^- > I^-$, $Cl^- > Br^- > NO_3^-$. The position of iodide is the only anomaly troubling the suggested correlation.

The correlation of acid hydrolysis rates in the $Co(NH_3)_5X^{2+}$ complexes with thermodynamic stability may, perhaps, be given an electronic explanation using another correlation. It is at least interesting to explore the fashion in which MO theory might be employed to rationalize the behavior of such a series of octahedral complexes. Rate of loss of the X group increases in the series $X = NO_2^- < NCS^- <$ $^-OOCCH_3$, $F^- < Cl^- < Br^- < I^-$. This corresponds to the spectrochemical series of the ligands [15] in these compounds. The spectrum of $Co(NH_3)_5NO_2^{2+}$ has the highest-energy first-visible absorption band, and the spectrum of $Co(NH_3)_5I^{2+}$ has the lowest. The energy of the first absorption band, roughly speaking, is a measure of the changing difference between the highest filled π-antibonding (π^*), or nonbonding, MO of this complex and the lowest-lying σ-antibonding (σ^*) level. This quantity may decrease by increased interactions between filled p levels on the ligand and filled t_{2g} levels on the metal leading to a higher-lying π^* level, or decreased σ interaction leading to a lower-lying σ^* level (and a corresponding higher σ-bonding level). In the event that the ligand has low-lying *empty* π orbitals, the difference may be increased since metal $\rightarrow$ ligand π interaction stabilizes the filled $t_{2g}(\pi)$ level mainly associated with the metal.

These are rough considerations. Correct analysis of the $Co(NH_3)_5$-X^{2+} problem requires recognition that the complexes are not strictly octahedral, and it is not a priori obvious what is the nature of the lowest spectral band. A detailed assignment of the spectra of the halopentammine complexes has been given.[16] The complexes have over-all symmetry C_{4v}, and this causes the octahedral t_{2g} levels to be split into an e pair and a b_2 level, and the e_g octahedral (σ^*) levels to be split into an a_1 and a b_1 level. If the z coordinate is chosen along the cobalt-halogen bond, the levels of these complexes can be associated with the familiar d orbital set as shown in Figure 3-2. In the halo complexes, where the filled p levels of the halogens may interact with the filled d_{xz} and d_{yz} levels of the metal, these two are π-antibonding and raised above d_{xy} (which remains formally nonbonding, assuming the NH_3 ligands have no effective π levels).

If we assume (quite plausibly [17]) that the position of the ligand in the spectrochemical series is strongly dependent on $\Delta\pi$, the π-antibonding

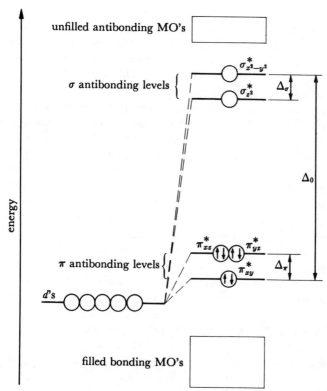

Figure 3-2   *MO diagram for the C_{4v}, $Co(NH_3)_5X^{n+}$ complexes. The z axis is chosen along the Co-X bond. (Not to scale.)*

orbital energy difference, a lower value of energy for the first band on going from F^- to I^- ligands may be correlated with increasing π interaction, leading to a higher π-antibonding level.   It is probably also correct that complexes containing ligands leading to high-energy bands have negative values for $\Delta\pi$.   These ligands include NCS^-, NO_2^-, and CN^-, with low-lying empty π orbitals which are very probably involved in important $d(\pi) \rightarrow L(\pi^*)$ interactions.

Figure 3-3 shows acid hydrolysis rates plotted as a function of the energy of the first spectral band.   The plot is assumed to closely approximate a plot of rates versus the negative of $\Delta\pi$.   On the right of the abscissa $\Delta\pi$ is positive; on the left it is negative.   The rate decreases with decreasing π interaction on the right ($I^- > Br^- > Cl^- > F^-$) because the filled π^* levels lead to a net *destabilization* of the complex, which is removed as the group is lost on going to the transition state. The rate continues to decrease on the left as $\Delta\pi$ becomes negative, because the complex is stabilized by π bonding, which must be overcome on going to the transition state. The slope of the line drawn in Figure 3-3 is (with axes expressed in consistent energy units) 1.3. The energy of the spectral band changes faster than the activation free energy.

The speculations in the previous paragraphs exemplify an approach to the theory of the lability of transition metal complexes that has enjoyed considerable popularity recently. In common with the frequently applied *crystal field theory*, we have focused attention on antibonding electrons. Clearly, the main determinant of the activation energy for substitution is the energy of the σ-*bonding* system. At the present crude stage of theoretical development, one of the best reasons for casting discussions in MO language is that designation of the octahedral t_{2g} and e_g levels as *antibonding* is a constant reminder of the important omission of the "bonds."

Since we shall return again to discussion of the role of the π electrons in octahedral complexes, a digression on the minimum constraints on construction of empirical MO theories of octahedral substitution will be given here as a critique of this first simple example. (Also, some attempt will be made to consider general difficulties that arise in attempts to understand electronic effects on reaction rates.) A molecular-orbital theory should be based on a spectroscopically validated energy-level scheme for the stable complex. It is very helpful if the energy levels can be identified in sufficient detail to give some hint as to the σ-bonding factor. Also, assumptions concerning secondary factors (such as the π-bonding capacity of ligands) should be validated from spectroscopic analysis. It is not usually sufficient to argue from the position of a ligand in the gross spectrochemical series, since this quantity involves an entirely *unknown* admixture of σ and π interactions in most cases.

Once electronic factors are understood, predicted trends must be corrected for environmental effects (for example, solvent) before they are compared to experiment. It may be lack of this correction that accounts for the anomalously slow reaction of the iodo complex indicated in Figure 3-3. Iodide is the least solvated of the halide ions in aqueous solution.

Finally, whenever electronic effects are analyzed, it is necessary to decide whether it is wiser to compare relative rates or activation energies. Electronic effects operate on the energy and not the entropy of activation, but the converse is not true. Environmental effects appear in both $\Delta S^{\ddagger}$ and $\Delta H^{\ddagger}$. Tobe et al.[18] have pointed out that relative rates may provide a more reliable basis for judging electronic effects. If solvent effects are thought of as being at all analogous to freezing or melting water around the reactants, the over-all free-energy change will be near zero at tem-

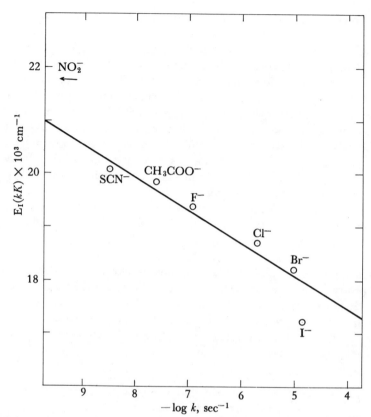

Figure 3-3   *Rates of acid hydrolysis of* $Co(NH_3)_5X^{2+}$ *ions as a function of the energy of the first ligand field spectral band.*

peratures near 273°K. However, the small free energy will result from cancellation of larger enthalpy and entropy terms. Thus, contributions to heats of activation arising from solvation effects are expected to be larger than contributions to free energies of activation, and free energies of activation may follow trends of electronic effects more closely.

3-5   EFFECTS OF CHARGE AND CHELATION

The effect of the over-all charge on the complex is easily predicted for D or I_d mechanisms. If there is a large amount of bond breaking in the transition state and the leaving group is developing a negative charge, increases of the over-all positive charge on the complex should increase the activation energy and thus reduce the rate. It is more difficult to predict the effect of charge on **a** processes. Increasing charge would probably facilitate nucleophilic attacks, but perhaps the charge effects would be small. Charge effects are small in reactions at Pt(II). It is also difficult to be sure one is measuring effects due to over-all charge on the complex, since each change of charge is produced by replacement of one ligand by another, a process that must produce changes in covalent bonding within the molecule in addition to the change of over-all charge. Thus it is probably wise to argue for a charge effect *only* if the effect can be demonstrated using a variety of ligand changes involving ligands of differing electronic types. Data are presented in Table 3-2 which show the role of charge in some acid hydrolysis reactions.

Examination of Table 3-2 shows that the charge effect in these acid hydrolysis reactions is of an order of magnitude of 10^2 to 10^3. The rate of substitution decreases as the over-all charge increases. This is fully consistent with expectation if the reactions are **d** but difficult to explain if the reactions are **a**. Defense of an **a** mechanism for any of the reactions would probably require the view that Table 3-2 displays electronic effects of ligand changes and not charge effects.

Another effect, apparent in Table 3-2, which deserves mention is the *chelation* effect observed on going from the ammine complexes to the

Table 3-2 *Rates of acid hydrolysis of Co(III) complexes reflecting variations of charge*

Complex	Ligand replaced	Rate constant, sec^{-1}	t, °C	Ref.
$Co(NH_3)_5Cl^{2+}$	Cl^-	6.7×10^{-6}	25	19
trans-$Co(NH_3)_4(OH_2)Cl^{2+}$	Cl^-	2.2×10^{-6}	20	20
cis-$Co(NH_3)_4Cl_2^+$	Cl^-	"very fast"	25	19
trans-$Co(NH_3)_4Cl_2^+$	Cl^-	1.8×10^{-3}	25	19
cis-$Co(en)_2(NH_3)Cl^{2+}$	Cl^-	1.4×10^{-6}	35	19
trans-$Co(en)_2(NH_3)Cl^{2+}$	Cl^-	4.0×10^{-7}	24	21
cis-$Co(en)_2Cl_2^+$	Cl^-	2.5×10^{-4}	25	19
trans-$Co(en)_2Cl_2^+$	Cl^-	3.2×10^{-5}	25	19
trans-$Co(en)_2(N_3)Cl^+$	Cl^-	2.5×10^{-4}	25	22
cis-$Co(en)_2(NO_2)Cl^+$	Cl^-	1.1×10^{-4}	25	22
$Co(NH_3)_5Br^{2+}$	Br^-	6.3×10^{-6}	25	23
trans-$Co(en)_2(NH_3)Br^{2+}$	Br^-	1.2×10^{-6}	25	21
trans-$Co(en)_2Br_2^+$	Br^-	1.4×10^{-4}	25	24
trans-$Co(en)_2(NO_2)Br^+$	Br^-	4.0×10^{-3}	25	25

ethylenediamine complexes. This change produces a reduction in rate. This is most probably a solvent effect. The organic groups tend to break up the solvation shell of the complex, whereas the complex makes greater demands on solvation on going to the transition state with separating charges. Thus factors contributing to poorer over-all solvation lead to lower hydrolysis rates. This view receives support from studies of deuteration effects. Solubility studies [26] on $Co(NH_3)_5Cl^{2+}$ in H_2O and D_2O show that deuteration of the solvent interferes with effective solvation of the complex. It was also shown that the acid hydrolysis rate is slower in D_2O. Solvent effects of this kind are predictable using any mechanism, but it would be interesting to see if these effects persist in nonaqueous solvents like N,N-dimethylformamide or dimethylsulfoxide, which are poorer anion solvents.

3-6 BASE HYDROLYSIS OF Co(III) COMPLEXES

The reactions of the Co(III) ammines with hydroxide, kinetically second order, might be most simply viewed as I_a processes. An apparent problem would be explanation of the unique position of the hydroxide ion as a nucleophile. But, it has been pointed out [27] that hydroxide ion is a privileged nucleophile in aqueous solution. It is the only one that can penetrate the second coordination sphere of the complex by the proton-transfer (Grottaus) conduction mechanism. Thus, it need not displace a water molecule.

There is, however, an alternative pathway for base hydrolysis which was first suggested by Garrick [28] and has been defended by Basolo and Pearson.[29] This alternate mechanism accounts for hydroxide acceleration on the basis of an acid-base reaction and postulates a transition state similar to that for the acid hydrolysis reaction. Postulation of this similarity is attractive, since many structure variations have quite similar effects on both acid and base hydrolysis reactions.

The Garrick mechanism is illustrated for $Co(NH_3)_5Cl^{2+}$ in Eq. (3-8). The first step is a fast proton transfer from an ammine ligand to hydroxide. The second step is the analog of the acid hydrolysis reaction and is rate-determining. If the first step is presumed to be at equilibrium, the base hydrolysis rate law becomes Eq. (3-9), where the measured second-order rate constant is the product of the equilibrium constant for the first step

$$Co(NH_3)_5Cl^{2+} + OH^- \rightleftharpoons Co(NH_3)_4(NH_2)Cl^+ + H_2O$$
$$Co(NH_3)_4(NH_2)Cl^+ + H_2O \xrightarrow{slow} Co(NH_3)_5OH^{2+} + Cl^- \qquad (3\text{-}8)$$

(K), and the first-order rate constant for the hydrolysis of the conjugate

$$\text{rate} = kK[\text{Co(NH}_3)_5\text{Cl}^+][\text{OH}^-] \qquad (3\text{-}9)$$

base of the complex (k).

The mechanism implicating the conjugate base of the complex is supported by a variety of indirect arguments and by two direct and compelling lines of evidence. The first and simplest is the behavior of complexes lacking an acidic proton. The rates of hydrolysis of *trans*-dinitro-bis(2,2'-bipyridine)cobalt(III) ion, *trans*-dichloro-bis(P,P,P'P'-tetraethyl-ethylenediphosphine)cobalt(III) ion,[30] *trans*-dichloro-bis(diarsine)cobalt(III) ion, and chloropentacyanocobalt(III) ion do not exhibit the hydroxide-dependent term. These results coupled with the generality of base acceleration in the complexes containing protons strongly suggest requirement of an acidic proton for rapid base hydrolysis.

The second important group of studies concerns the nature of the entering group. The $\mathbf{I_a}$ mechanism requires that the hydroxide ion be the entering group, whereas the conjugate base mechanism allows a water molecule, or even another anion, to function as the entering group. Hydroxide is only required in the first step of Eq. (3-8). In aqueous solution it is difficult to distinguish hydroxide entry from water entry because of facile proton transfer. It is not surprising that the first competition studies were carried out in a nonaqueous medium. Pearson and co-workers[31] studied reaction (3-10) in dimethylsulfoxide. They found

$$\text{trans-Co(en)}_2(\text{NO}_2)\text{Cl}^{2+} + \text{NO}_2^- \rightarrow \text{trans-Co(en)}_2(\text{NO}_2)_2^+ + \text{Cl}^- \qquad (3\text{-}10)$$

that the rate was first order, independent of nitrite concentration. On introduction of small amounts of hydroxide, the rate of chloride release was spectacularly accelerated but the product *remained trans*-Co(en)$_2$-(NO$_2$)$_2^+$. Since it was shown that Co(en)$_2$(NO$_2$)OH$^+$ was not labile under the reaction conditions, it followed that the initial entering group was either the nitrite ion or a molecule of dimethylsulfoxide, not hydroxide.

An ingenious experiment was devised by Green and Taube[32] to show that hydroxide need not be the entering group in the *aqueous* base-catalyzed reaction. If the reaction is run in water enriched in ^{18}O, and hydroxide functions as the entering group, the ^{16}O/^{18}O ratio of hydroxide ion should correspond to the ^{16}O/^{18}O ratio in the hydrolysis product, barring relatively small kinetic-isotope effects. The ^{16}O/^{18}O ratio in hydroxide is 1.040 times the ratio in water, according to results for the equilibrium $\text{H}_2^{16}\text{O} + {}^{18}\text{OH}^- = \text{H}_2^{18}\text{O} + {}^{16}\text{OH}^-$. The increase in the ^{16}O/^{18}O ratio of the hydroxo product (compared to the solvent) was 1.0056 for base hydrolysis of Co(NH$_3$)$_5$Cl^{2+}, 1.0056 for base hydrolysis of

$Co(NH_3)_5Br^{2+}$, 1.0056 for base hydrolysis of $Co(NH_3)_5NO_3^{2+}$, and 0.9975 for base hydrolysis of $Co(NH_3)_5F^{2+}$. Green and Taube pointed out that the kinetic-isotope effect is expected to favor ^{16}O so that the factor 1.040 probably represents a minimum if hydroxide is the entering group, and 1.000 should represent a minimum if water is the entering group. The result favors water entry in all four cases. The common value for the chloro, bromo, and nitrato complexes suggests that a common intermediate reacts with water in these cases, as would be the case if the second step of Eq. (3-8) were actually a two-step **D** process. Fluoride, on the other hand, appears to influence the process of water entry—a result that could be rationalized using an I_d model.

Assuming that Eq. (3-8) is a correct formulation, it is interesting to attempt to estimate the magnitude of k in Eq. (3-9). The acidity constant of the Co(III)-ammine complexes must be less than or equal to 10^{-14} and may be as low as 10^{-18}, according to deductions from the rate of deuterium-hydrogen exchange.[33] If this is correct, k for $Co(NH_3)_4$-$(NH_2)Cl^+$ may be as high as 10^6 sec^{-1}, but Basolo and Pearson give the minimum estimate of 10^2 sec^{-1} in their recent review.[30] If we consider that acid hydrolysis rates of related complexes do not exceed 1 sec^{-1} [the direct comparison is $Co(NH_3)_5Cl^{2+}$, which is 10^{-4} sec^{-1}], it is clear that the conjugate base mechanism implies a large accelerating effect produced by the presence of an NH_2^- ligand in the complex.

3-7 THE EFFECTS OF NONLABILE LIGANDS

Adoption of the conjugate-base hypothesis as the description of base hydrolysis focuses attention on the spectacular effect of the presence of a nonlabile substituent in the complex, in that case NH_2^-. An immediate problem is to rationalize the electronic effect of that substituent, but there is a more general reason for considering electronic effects of ligands other than the leaving-group effects. A satisfactory theory of their role promises another test of the consistency of the general hypothesis concerning **d** transition states in hydrolysis. Hopefully, the discussion of electronic effects of substituents need not be perfectly circular. That is, the electronic role of ligands should be at least in part predictable from *evidence external to the kinetics of octahedral substitutions* (for example, spectra).

It is important that the electronic effects of substituents be identified by study of a series of closely related complexes. An appropriate set is found in the *cis*- and *trans*-$Co(en)_2(A)X^+$ ions, where X is the leaving group (Cl^- or Br^-) and A is a nonlabile anionic substituent. The acid hydrolysis reaction of these ions has been studied over a wide range of A groups. (Data for "neutral molecule" A groups are available, but these confuse the problem by changing the over-all charge on the complex to +2.) The first rationalization of the results assigned the role of the A groups as those were known from organic reactions. Most simply, A groups could be identified as electron-donating or electron-withdrawing. More subtly, these effects were ascribed to conjugative or inductive mechanisms. The rationale for the assignments is given by Ingold et al.[22] Figure 3-4 shows the log of the acid hydrolysis rate constants at 25°C plotted as a function of the nature of the A ligand, with chloride as the leaving group. The A's are ordered from most strongly electron donating on the left to most electron withdrawing on the right. There is a rate minimum in the

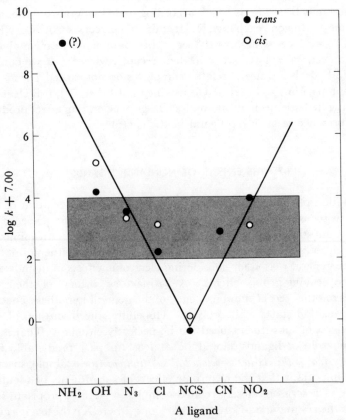

Figure 3-4   *Rate constants for acid hydrolysis at 25° in the series cis- and trans-$Co(en)_2(A)Cl^+$ as a function of the nonlabile ligand A.   (Data from Ref. 22 except A = CN point from Ref. 28.)*

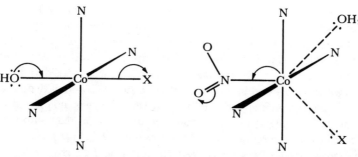

(a) lone pair donation from ligand assists heterolytic fission of bond to leaving group

(b) acceptance of electrons from Co assists attack of nucleophile by lowering electron density at Co center

Figure 3-5   *Assistance of acid hydrolysis by nonlabile ligands.*

middle, and *both* good electron donors and good electron acceptors appear to increase the acid hydrolysis rate. Ingold and his collaborators have suggested that the two-branch curve implies a dichotomy of mechanism. According to the argument, electron-donor A ligands supply electron density as the leaving group departs with its bonding pair, thereby lowering the activation energy for bond breaking (**d** processes in our notation). Conversely, an electron-acceptor ligand reduces the electron density at cobalt, thereby lowering the activation energy for nucleophilic attack (**a** mechanism). The conjugative behavior of —OH and —NO_2 shown in Figure 3-5 illustrates these opposite effects and the different transition states proposed to explain acceleration in both cases.

Note that the suggested explanation of the role of good electron-acceptor ligands such as the nitrite ion requires quite significant assistance from the entering group in the transition state, since the over-all acceleration must result from lower activation energy due to bond formation. Asperger and Ingold [35] suggest that acid hydrolysis of *trans*-$Co(en)_2(NO_2)Cl^{2+}$ proceeds with formation of the Co—OH_2 bond in the lead over fission of the Co—Cl bond (the **a** process). This implies an exception to the generalization concerning **d** activation and, therefore, predicts a detectable role for the entering group.

In a series of studies [5, 36-38] an effort was made to detect a role for the entering group in acid hydrolysis or related solvolysis reactions of *trans*-$Co(en)_2(NO_2)Cl^+$ and *trans*-$Co(en)_2(NO_2)Br^+$ and in the reverse reactions (anations) of these complexes. In reactions in dimethylformamide, no kinetic effect of large concentrations (10 mole per cent) of neutral nucleophiles (for example, H_2O, pyridine, urea) could be found. Rates of solvolysis by the solvents dimethylformamide, methanol, and dimethylsulfoxide were surprisingly similar to the acid hydrolysis rate, *and* the solvolysis rates of the nitro complexes varied in the *same* way as those of *trans*-$Co(en)_2Cl_2^+$ as the solvent changed. The rate of anation of *trans*-$Co(en)_2(NO_2)OH_2^{2+}$ in various solvents was found to be nearly insensitive to the nature of the anion (ion-association effects were considered). Some of this work is discussed in more detail in Sections 3-9 and 3-10 on reactions in nonaqueous solvents, but, briefly, these results suggest no more profound role for the entering group in reactions of nitro-substituted complexes than in reactions of chloro-substituted complexes. *It has not proved possible to obtain support for the "two-mechanism" interpretation of Figure 3-4.*

Although the suggestions contained in Figure 3-5 are attractive because they find precedent in organic experience, the conflicting evidence concerning electron-acceptor substituents requires consideration of alternative explanations of the pattern in Figure 3-4. It would be especially interesting to see if more direct use could be made of spectroscopically validated MO schemes to assign electronic roles. We shall begin with the "electron-donor" substituents like —OH, rather than immediately approaching the trouble spot.

If we return to consideration of the spectra of $Co(NH_3)_5X^{2+}$ ions, a new difficulty emerges. In these spectra π-donor interaction in the ground state is much larger when $X^- = Br^-$ or Cl^- than when $X^- = OH^-$ or F^- (the last two having very similar spectra). The better conjugative electron donor A, as judged from the kinetics, is the poorer π donor, according to the spectra. But, the kinetically important term is the difference in energy between the ground state and the transition state. The kinetic order of assisting ligands is not that of the spectrochemical series but is shifted in favor of ligands near the bottom of the nephelauxetic series.[39] These are ligands that result in the smallest decrease in value of the interelectronic-repulsion parameters. Perhaps they are kinetically effective because the large interelectronic-repulsion terms in the ground state can be reduced by delocalization as an *empty orbital* is made available by the leaving group in the transition state. (This suggestion will prove useful later in accounting for effects of the electron-donor ligands on stereochemistry and in accounting for the smaller role they play in reactions of second and third transition series complexes, where interelectronic-repulsion parameters are smaller.) The role of electron-donor substituents may be viewed in large part as a ground-state repulsion that is reduced in a transition state with an empty orbital.

The electron-acceptor ligands stabilize the complex by π bonding ($\Delta\pi$ is negative in $Co(NH_3)_5(NO_2)^{2+}$). It is plausible to suggest that departure of the leaving group would lead to stronger σ bonds and, as a result, an increase in π overlap strengthening the π bonding. There is some independent evidence for π acceptors stabilizing complexes of reduced coordination number. The best documented five-coordinate intermediate in Co(III) substitution chemistry [40a] is $Co(CN)_5^{2-}$. Very recent evidence supports the stability of the five-coordinate intermediate $Co(NH_3)_4SO_3^+$.[40b] An effect similar to that envisioned here was required to explain [41] CO exchange results in $Mn(CO)_5X$. It should be noted that an important difference between these octahedral complexes and the organic systems used for reference in generating the explanation in Figure 3-5 is that here the substituent is attached *directly* to the atom experiencing substitution.

This alternative to the first discussion of A effects only elaborates the explanation of the effects of conjugative electron donors. There is no real conflict. But, it shows that an alternate account may be given of the effect of electron-acceptor ligands which is consistent with the evidence for the **d** transition state. We shall not attempt final adjudication of the dispute over the role of these groups. It is more important to make some cautionary comments on the source of this difficulty. Returning to Figure 3-4, we see that it seems reasonable to offer a different reading from that indicated by the two lines. Perhaps the correct approach to this figure is to consider all the rates in the shaded area similar except for small differences which may be due as much to solvent and other environmental effects as to electronic effects. Then the problem would be explanation of acceleration by —OH and —NH$_2$, which is probably satisfactorily accomplished, and explanation of retardation by —NCS, which remains a mystery. It is true that no simple two-branch curve can be drawn through a plot of *activation energies* versus A groups.

3-8   Co(III) STEREOCHEMISTRY

The stereochemistry of the octahedron is richer than that of the tetrahedron. The straightforward connection between steric course and mechanism that characterizes substitutions at carbon centers is lost in octahedral systems. To illustrate the richness of possibilities, the systems with two bidentate ligands like $Co(en)_2(A)X^+$ are convenient, where X designates the leaving group and A a nonlabile reference ligand. The entering group will be designated Y.

The simplest case is that of a **D** mechanism. The **D** mechanism includes a five-coordinate intermediate, and the most probable geometries are those of known five-coordinate complexes—the square pyramid and the trigonal bipyramid. Consider first the intermediates derived from *trans*-$Co(en)_2(A)X^+$ shown in Figure 3-6. The square-pyramidal intermediate has an open face where the leaving group was located and is expected to yield 100 per cent *trans* product by addition of the new group

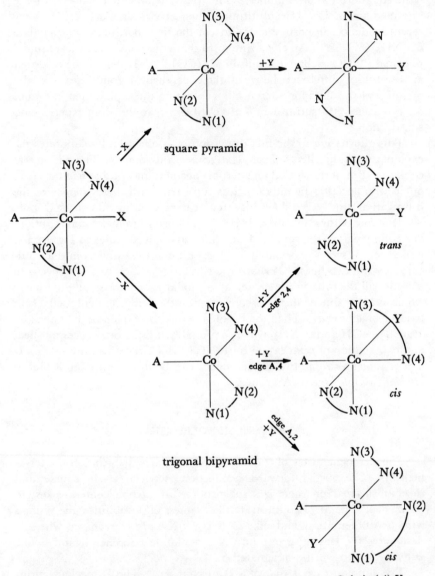

Figure 3-6   *Stereochemistry of a* **D** *substitution in trans-Co(en)₂(A)X.*

on the open face. The trigonal-bipyramidal intermediate has three nearly equivalent directions for addition of the entering group, between N(2) and N(4), between N(2) and A, or between N(4) and A. The two adjacent to A yield *cis* products, whereas the third yields a *trans* product. In the case of a *cis* starting material, the situation may be more complex since *cis*-Co(en)$_2$(A)X$^+$ may be optically active. Figure 3-7 illustrates the consequences for the two distinct trigonal-bipyramidal intermediates derived from optically active *cis*-Co(en)$_2$(A)X$^+$. (The square pyramid will lead to a *cis* product with retention of activity.)

All **I** and **A** mechanisms may be treated together, since the stereo-

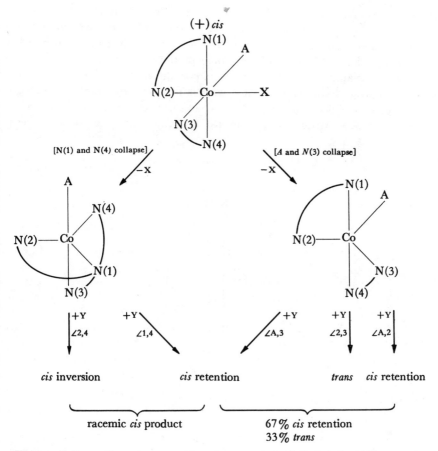

Figure 3-7 *Stereochemistry of* **D** *substitution in* (+)*cis-Co(en)$_2$A(X) through the trigonal bipyramidal intermediate.*

chemistry will be determined by the initial direction of attack of the entering group.   A simple case is Y attack through any one of the edges of the octahedron *cis* to the leaving group.   All these attacks yield products of the same geometry as the starting complex, including retention of any optical activity.   The result is similar to that for the square-pyramidal intermediate.   If the attack of Y is *trans* to the leaving group (that is, from the "back" of the complex), complicated rearrangements are possible.   If Y is thought of as entering one of the *trans* edges (more probably, the group enters through an octahedral face, but the net results are ultimately the same and consideration of edges is easier to visualize) of the octahedron, a group already on that edge must shift into the position being vacated by the leaving group, making a place for Y.   This process is called an *edge displacement* by Ingold and his collaborators,[42] which focuses attention on this aspect of *trans* attack.   The results of possible *trans* attacks on optically active *cis*-$Co(en)_2(A)X^+$ are illustrated in Figure 3-8.   We see that attack on one edge leads to *cis* product with retention, one leads to *cis* product with inversion, and one leads to a *trans* product.

These examples illustrate several important general points.   First, it is clear that substantial molecular rearrangements can lead to no observable steric change.   Second, any of the mechanisms may lead to no observable steric change.   More usefully, optical inversion can occur only in the

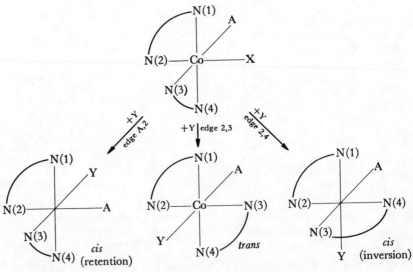

Figure 3-8   *Steric consequences of trans attacks on* $(+)cis$-$Co(en)_2(A)X$.

	no edge displacement			
steric change	no steric change			
cis ⇌ trans	D ⇌ L	D ⇌ D / L ⇌ L	cis ⇌ cis	trans ⇌ trans
edge displacement				

Figure 3-9   *Relation of observable steric change in complexes of the type Coen₂AX to edge displacements.   (From Ref. 42.)*

case of an **I** or **A** mechanism utilizing a particular *trans* attack.* If it could be assumed that attacks at various edges of intermediates were deter-- mined statistically, further deductions could be made for **D** processes, but the assumption is probably not warranted. The nature of the groups should have some orienting effect. Figure 3-9 shows, in general, the complicated relationship between microscopic steric changes (edge displacements) and observable steric changes for the **I** and **A** processes.

Turning to the experimental results, the best characterized systems are again the acid hydrolysis reactions of *cis*- and *trans*-$Co(en)_2(A)Cl^{n+}$ ions (here A need not be an anionic ligand). The results are collected in Table 3-3, together with some results for the analogous compounds having Br^- as the leaving group. It appears that retention of both optical activity and the original geometric isomerism is the nearly general result. Only in *trans* compounds with certain A groups is isomerization observed. Ingold et al.[22] have offered a stereokinetic rule for these compounds: *Retention* occurs unless there is a π donor A group in the *trans* position. Retention is consistent with the hypothesis of **d** activation, if the mechanism is **D** and the intermediate is a square-pyramid. It also seems the most likely consequence of an I_d process, because the leaving group is weakly bound in the transition state (making a position available) but probably also close enough to its original site to prevent the collapse of the complex toward a trigonal bipyramid (which would facilitate *trans* attack).

---

* There are a small number of interesting examples of inversion. See J. C. Bailar and W. Auten, *J. Am. Chem. Soc.*, **56**, 774 (1934); R. D. Archer and J. C. Bailar, *J. Am. Chem. Soc.*, **83**, 812 (1961); and F. P. Dwyer, A. M. Sargeson, and I. K. Reid, *J. Am. Chem. Soc.*, **85**, 1215 (1963). These are complicated by the involvement of base. Probably any mechanism from I_d to **A** would be consistent with the available results.

Table 3-3 [a]   *Stereochemical consequences of acid*
hydrolyses of cis- and trans-Co(en)$_2$(A)X$^{+ \ or \ 2+}$

X	A	*cis*	Retention of optical activity
cis Cl$^-$	OH$^-$	100	
cis Cl$^-$	N$_3^-$	100	
cis Cl$^-$	Cl$^-$	100	yes
cis Cl$^-$	NCS$^-$	100	yes
cis Cl$^-$	NH$_3$	100	yes
cis Cl$^-$	NO$_2^-$	100	yes
cis-Br$^-$	NCS$^-$	100	
cis-Br$^-$	NH$_3$	100	
cis-NO$_3^-$	NH$_3$	100	
trans-Cl$^-$	OH$^-$	some	
trans-Cl$^-$	N$_3^-$	20	
trans-Cl$^-$	Cl$^-$	some	
trans-Cl$^-$	NCS$^-$	50	
trans-Cl$^-$	NH$_3$	0	
trans-Cl$^-$	NO$_2^-$	0	
trans-Br$^-$	NCS$^-$	43	
trans-Br$^-$	NH$_3$	0	
trans-Br$^-$	NO$_2^-$	0	
trans-NO$_3^-$	NH$_3$	0	

[a] Data from Ref. 22.

Pearson and Basolo [43] were the first to explain the role of π-donor ligands in inducing isomerization. It was argued above that these ligands accelerate acid hydrolysis by π donation into empty orbitals. If we consider the complex to have approximate C_{4v} symmetry with the leaving group on the z axis, the orbitals being vacated above have p_z and d_{z^2} components. For π donor orbitals in the *trans* position, overlap with the vacated orbitals will be zero unless the complex rearranges to the trigonal bipyramid. We need not be sure whether the trigonal bipyramid is an intermediate on a **D** path or not, since the rate results suggest that π donation is already important in the transition state. A π donor in the *cis* position may overlap, if only poorly, without any rearrangement.

The group with the most spectacular effects on rates, NH$_2^-$, also appears to have the most spectacular effects on stereochemistry. Rearrangements are extensive in base hydrolysis reactions even in *cis* complexes. The patterns have been elaborated in careful studies, especially by Tobe, and are reviewed by Ingold et al.[44] It is probably premature to attempt a detailed analysis, since a *new unique position* is introduced in base hydrolysis, namely, the amide position from which the proton is lost. There is no information available as to the relationship of the position of proton loss to the A and X positions. (Recent nmr studies by Buckingham and Sargeson [45] promise to establish which ammine protons are most labile at high pH, and this may lead to identification of the amide site.) Pearson and Basolo [45a] have shown that the observed stereochemical results are as consistent with expectations based on a conjugate-base **D** mechanism as they are with those based on an **I** mechanism. [44] The treatment involves the reasonable assumptions that minimum atomic motion is involved in reaching the intermediate and that the amide group must be in the trigonal plane of a trigonal-bipyramid intermediate in order to take advantage of the *d* orbital which is emptied by leaving-group departure. Two types of trigonal-bipyramidal intermediate may be derived from the *cis* isomer of $Co(en)_2(A)X$ (see Fig. 3-7), but only one from the *trans* isomer (see Fig. 3-6). A *trans* product may arise only from the common intermediate, thus the rule may be formulated that the *cis* isomer must never give less *cis* product than does the *trans* form.

An especially interesting study is that of the isomerization and water-exchange reactions of *cis*- and *trans*-$Co(en)_2(NH_3)OH_2^{3+}$ reported by Martin and Tobe. [46] The conjunction of exchange data with data on stereochemical rearrangement gives some indication of the relative ease of substitution with or without steric change. It was found that water exchange takes place only about 80 times faster than isomerization of the *trans* complex or racemization of the optically active *cis* complex. These results suggest that the substitution path without rearrangement enjoys a significant, but not a great, energetic advantage over the path with rearrangement. One example from the literature showing the existence of a preference for a particular attack pathway is Sargeson's report [47] that isomerization of *cis*-$Co(en)_2(OH_2)Cl^+$ to the *trans* form proceeds at the same rate as racemization. The complex does not take advantage of one of the pathways (see Figures 3-7 and 3-8) for racemization without conversion to the *trans* form.

3-9 REACTIONS IN NONAQUEOUS SOLVENTS

In the last few years, reactions of several of the cobaltammine complexes have been studied in some of the more polar nonaqueous solvents. These include methanol, N,N-dimethylformamide, dimethylsulfoxide, N,N-dimethylacetamide, acetone, and tetramethylene sulfone. These solvents are of moderate dielectric constant, and conductance studies on *simple* electrolytes have shown many to behave as strong electrolytes.

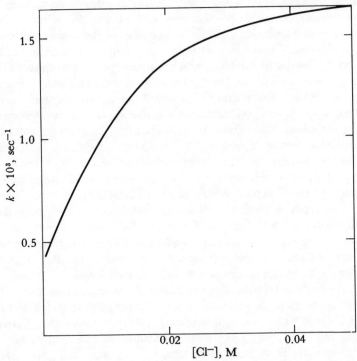

Figure 3-10   *First order rate constants for radiochloride exchange in cis-Co(en)₂Cl₂⁺ in methanol at 35° as a function of the chloride ion concentration. (Ref. 48.)*

The kinetics of substitution of one anionic ligand by another are more complicated than in aqueous solution. The entering ligand does appear in the rate laws, but simple rate laws are not common. A good example is the radiochloride-exchange reaction of *cis*-Co(en)₂Cl₂⁺ in methanol.[48] When this reaction is studied with excess chloride, the observed pseudo first-order rate constant increases as the chloride concentration is increased from zero, but reaches a limiting value at about 0.02 M (Figure 3-10). The zero chloride intercept is not zero. This behavior may be interpreted by assuming that *cis*-Co(en)₂Cl₂⁺ forms an outer-sphere complex *cis*-Co(en)₂Cl₂⁺ · · · Cl⁻, which reacts in a first-order process at a rate different from the free ion. The appropriate rate law is Eq. (3-11), and

$$\text{rate} = k_1[\text{Co(en)}_2\text{Cl}_2^+] + k_2[(\text{Co(en)}_2\text{Cl}_2^+) \cdot \cdot \cdot \text{Cl}^-] \quad (3\text{-}11)$$

the concentration of the outer-sphere complex would be determined by the equilibrium equation (3-12).   Thus the over-all rate is chloride-dependent

$$K = \frac{[(Co(en)_2Cl_2^+) \cdots Cl^-]}{[Co(en)_2Cl_2^+][Cl^-]} \qquad (3-12)$$

until all the complex has been converted to outer-sphere ion pair.   A fit to the kinetic data is obtained with $K = 300$ mole^{-1}.   Independent conductance experiments [48] give $K = 280$ mole^{-1}.

Figure 3-10 shows that the ion aggregate does not react much faster than the free ion.   The reaction of the ion aggregate may or may not involve the outer-sphere chloride in an intimate way.   We do not know if the chloride that finally enters the first sphere is the one originally in the outer sphere or if methanol enters first.   The reaction of the "free" complex ion has the appearance of the methanol equivalent of acid hydrolysis, with the same mechanistic possibilities of either a **D** substitution or a *solvent* attack followed by entry of an anion into the solvo complex.

The pattern described for chloride exchange of *cis*-Co(en)$_2$Cl$_2^+$ in methanol is common.   The results of analysis of the behavior of *cis*- and *trans*-Co(en)$_2$Cl$_2^+$ in methanol, dimethylformamide, and dimethylacetamide are summarized in Table 3-4, which gives rates of chloride exchange or geometric isomerization.   Reactions are seen to proceed at comparable rates in both "free" complex and outer-sphere ion pair.   It is interesting that outer-sphere association constants are much smaller for the *trans* isomer than for the *cis*.

The three solvents discussed so far form reasonably stable complexes themselves and, *after ion association is included, the mechanism problem is analogous to acid hydrolysis.*   Tetramethylene sulfone, on the other hand, is without doubt a much poorer ligand.   In the reaction studied in tetramethylene sulfone,[25] no entering-group-independent paths were observed. First-order rate constants for water entry, thiocyanate entry, and chloride entry into *trans*-Co(en$_2$)(NO$_2$)Br$^+$ in the sulfone solvent are plotted against entering-group concentration in Figure 3-11.   The water rate is exaggerated for visibility.   Note that the absence of a finite rate at the intercept excludes both reaction by way of a solvent-containing intermediate and reaction by a **D** path as important contributors.   Conversely, the chloride result exhibiting a limiting rate suggests that *the entering group dependence is associated with outer-sphere aggregation* phenomena, and this suggestion is reinforced by the observation that the water-entry rate is nearly a linear function of the water-volume fraction over the entire range of sulfone-water mixtures.   If the cation-solvating capabilities of water and the sulfone are comparable, the volume fraction should be the determinant of the composition of the outer coordination sphere.

Table 3-4 Ion association constants and first-order rate constants for chloride exchange or isomerization of cis- and trans-$Co(en)_2Cl_2^+$ in three solvents [a]

	K_{cis}, mole^{-1}	K_{trans}, mole^{-1}	k_{cis}, sec^{-1}	k_{trans}, sec^{-1}	k_{cis}IP, sec^{-1}	k_{trans}IP, sec^{-1}
Methanol (35°)	300	—	7.7×10^{-5}	5.3×10^{-6}	1.4×10^{-3}	—
Dimethylformamide (60°)	1800	30	—	5×10^{-5}	1.3×10^{-3}	1.5×10^{-2}
Dimethylacetamide (60°)	1700	—	2.8×10^{-5}	5×10^{-6}	6.8×10^{-5}	—

[a] Data from M. L. Tobe, Ref. 48. Dashes indicate information unavailable, not necessarily that the quantities are small.

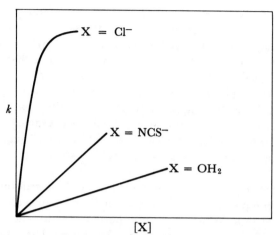

Figure 3-11 *Dependence of the first-order rate constants for substitution reactions of trans-Co(en)₂(NO₂)Br⁺ on the concentration of the entering group X. The slower rates are exaggerated for visibility.* (*Ref. 25.*)

An especially interesting group of experiments [5] concerned the *anation* reaction of *trans*-Coen₂NO₂OH₂²⁺ with NO₃⁻, Br⁻, Cl⁻, and SCN⁻ in a solvent system of tetramethylene sulfone with a little water. The reactions were nearly anion-independent, except at very low anion concentration. Parallel conductance studies indicated that at least 1:1 outersphere complexes were formed (for example, Co(en)₂(NO₂)OH₂²⁺ · · · Cl⁻). Probably higher aggregates were present (for example, Co(en)₂(NO₂)OH₂²⁺ · · · Cl₂²⁻). In these circumstances, it is difficult to assign rates for individual aggregate species with assurance, but the raw experimental data contained the startling result that entry of Br⁻, NO₃⁻, and Cl⁻ took place at the same rate and that SCN⁻ entered half as fast. After assignments of degrees of aggregation, it was concluded that, in the 1:1 outersphere complexes, Br⁻, NO₃⁻, and Cl⁻ did indeed enter at the same rate and that thiocyanate was slower by a factor of 2 to 4. Thus no substantial differences between entering groups could be observed. A similar result over a wider range of solvent systems was later reported by Hughes and Tobe.[38] These last results are important, because they imply strongly that a *complex* containing an NO₂ group can react by an I_d process. Despite the early interpretation of the electronic effect of a π-acceptor ligand, it appears that strong bonding with an entering group is not required. This conclusion has received reinforcement from a study [36] of the reactions in dimethylsulfoxide, dimethylformamide, and methanol, which are the analogs of the acid hydrolysis process, that is, the reaction involving replacement of an anionic ligand by a molecule of the solvent. The solvent dependence of the solvolysis rate is the same for complexes containing π-donor nonlabile ligands as it is for complexes containing π-acceptor nonlabile ligands. The best explanation is that both complexes involve the solvent in the reaction in the same way. That the role of the solvent is small is suggested again by the fact that the solvent dependence is relatively small. Incidentally, it is interesting that the effect of the A (nonlabile) ligand in trans-$Co(en)_2(A)Cl^+$ on the rate of SCN^- entry in dimethylformamide for A = NO_2^-, SCN^-, and Cl^- suggests the A effects of Figure 3-4.[37] Thus, gross A effects do not appear to be solvent-dependent.

In summary, once allowance is made for the enhanced importance of outer-sphere complexing, reactions in the polar nonaqueous solvents look very similar to those in water. An important role for the solvent as a reactive ligand remains a feature of the chemistry. The solvolysis rates cover a surprisingly small range, the hypothesis of dissociative activation may be systematically applied, and it is of importance to consider I_d processes as well as D processes.

3-10   EVIDENCE FOR I_d PROCESSES

In the preceding sections, we have reviewed the general behavior of Co(III)-ammine complexes and have emphasized the consistency of this large body of evidence with the model of a dissociative activation process in which the entering ligand does not participate to any large degree in determining the activation energy. There are two distinct paths, the I_d and the D paths, which are similar in intimate mechanism but different in stoichiometric mechanism. We must now investigate the possibility of learning about the stoichiometric mechanism of some Co(III)-ammine reactions. As suggested in Section 1-6, we may expect small differences in structure or environment to lead to a shift from I_d to D. In this section, we shall consider systems for which some definite evidence of an I_d process is discernible.

The substitution reactions of trans-$Co(en)_2(NO_2)Br^-$ in tetramethylene sulfone solution are most probably I_d reactions. Figure 3-11 indicated that there was no entering-group-independent path, thereby excluding a D process as a significant pathway. It might be argued that the reactions are I_a, but the subsequent experience with related compounds in the sulfone is inconsistent with this.[5] Furthermore, the simplest explanation of the entering-group dependence follows from postulating an I_d path. There seems to be a definite reactant preassembly requirement. The chloride curve is certainly to be explained on the basis of outer-sphere association, and the dependence of water entry on the volume fraction of water suggests that water occupancy of outer-sphere positions determines rate of water entry. Most significantly, the different outer-sphere aggregates react at approximately the *same* rate without regard to whether H_2O or Cl^- is in the reactive position. In the dry sulfone, chloride entry at 35°C reaches a limiting rate of $\sim 4 \times 10^{-3}$ sec^{-1} only a little below the rate of acid hydrolysis in *water*, 4×10^{-3} sec^{-1} at 25°C.

Posey and Taube [49] studied ^{18}O isotope fractionation in the Hg^{2+}-catalyzed hydrolysis of halogenopentamminecobalt(III) complexes. This fast removal of the halide led to $Co(NH_3)_5OH_2^{3+}$ enriched by a factor of 1.012 in ^{16}O over the ^{16}O content of the solvent. This factor was found to be *independent* of the leaving group, and it was argued that this implied that the water-entry step was independent of both leaving group and mercuric ion. Thus it appeared that Hg^{2+} provided a means of generating the reactive **D** intermediate. (The fact that the fractionation factors are leaving-group dependent in Ag^+- and Tl^{3+}-catalyzed reactions shows the result to be nontrivial.) If the Hg^{2+}-catalyzed reaction generates the intermediate of the **D** path, then it is interesting to compare product distributions in the Hg^{2+}-catalyzed reaction to those obtained in the ordinary acid hydrolysis. Sargeson [50] reports the D-*cis* and *trans* isomer distribution in the Hg^{2+}-catalyzed aquation of D-*cis*-Co(en)$_2$Cl$_2^+$ to be 70 per cent D-*cis* and 30 per cent *trans*-Co(en)$_2$(Cl)OH$_2^{2+}$. Figure 3-6 shows the predicted distribution from formation of a trigonal-bipyramidal five-coordinate intermediate followed by randomized water attack. The prediction is 67 per cent D-*cis* and 33 per cent *trans*, very close to the experimental results. The case for an intermediate in the mercury-catalyzed reaction is strong. This is to be contrasted to the *uncatalyzed* acid hydrolysis reaction which gives 100 per cent D-*cis*-chloroaquo-bis-(ethylenediamine)cobalt(III) ion from the D-*cis*-dichloro complex. At the very least a different intermediate is involved, and more probably the normal acid hydrolysis is I_d. The leaving chloride is still present in the product-determining stage, blocking formation of the trigonal bipyramid. A water molecule replaces chloride in *cis* attack. A very similar indication of I_d acid hydrolysis of $Coen_2(N_3)_2^+$ emerges from experiments of Loeliger and Taube.[51] (The intermediate of the **D** path could, apparently, be generated by reaction of an azide ligand with HNO_2.)

A final example for which evidence supporting an I_d process exists is the anation of $Co(NH_3)_5OH_2^{3+}$ with halides and related ligands. The case is complicated but perhaps exemplary of a general approach for establishing I_d mechanisms.

The first important piece of information is that equilibria of the halide anation processes are such that significant amounts of $Co(NH_3)_5X^{2+}$ complexes are present at equilibrium with only modest total X^- concentrations. This implies, minimally, that the rates of anation are comparable to their reverse acid hydrolyses. Let us assume, for the moment, that the anation reaction does proceed by a **D** mechanism. The rate of anation would be determined by two things: (1) the rate at which water is lost to form the five-coordinate intermediate and (2) the relative rate of reaction of the intermediate with water and the anion, since reaction of the intermediate with water leads back to the aquo complex and no net reaction. The first rate is known from study of ^{18}O exchange.[52] Also, rates of aquation give the rate at which the five-coordinate intermediate is formed from the $Co(NH_3)_5X^{2+}$ species. Using these rates of formation of the intermediate in conjunction with the known equilibrium constant, it is possible to compute the fraction of the intermediate that reacts with water and fraction that reacts with an anion. In the case of SCN^- anation, the percentage of the intermediate reacting with the anion should (on this model) be at least 5 per cent at 0.1 M SCN^- to 15 per cent at 0.5 M SCN^-. But, we noted in Section 3-2 that Pearson and Moore[2] were unable to detect *any* (± 2 per cent) direct SCN^- entry into $Co(NH_3)_5NO_3^{2+}$ or $Co(NH_3)_5Br^{2+}$ during hydrolysis. The entire reaction went through $Co(NH_3)_5OH_2^{3+}$. Defense of a **D** mechanism for anation requires the curious postulate that NO_3^- or Br^- somehow interfere with the ability of the five-coordinate intermediate to react with another anion. The **D** model makes explicit predictions about the reactivity of the intermediate that cannot be realized.

In anations of $Co(NH_3)_5OH_2^{3+}$ with SO_4^{2-} or $H_2PO_4^-$, a limiting rate is reached at high anion concentration which correlates with the formation of the first outer-sphere complex (ion pair). This means that in three cases we may measure the rate of ligand entry from the second coordination sphere, since from this point of view we may include water exchange also. If the rate of water exchange is taken to be 1, the relative rate of SO_4^{2-} entry from the outer-sphere ion pair[53] is 0.31, and the rate of entry[54] of $H_2PO_4^-$ is 0.13. In anations with SCN^- and Cl^-, limiting rates are not reached, probably because a second and even a third anion may enter the outer coordination sphere.[55] Using values for the first outer-sphere association constant chosen according to the evaluation in Ref. 55, we find that when the ratio of $Co(NH_3)_5OH_2^{3+} \cdot \cdot \cdot X^-$/ $Co(NH_3)_5OH_2^{3+}$ is to be 10, the rate of anion entry relative to the rate of water entry is 0.11 for chloride and 0.20 for thiocyanate.[55] Since the first outer-sphere association constant for SCN^- appears to be closer to the second than in the other cases, this last figure probably includes a significant contribution from the reaction of $Co(NH_3)_5OH_2^{3+} \cdot \cdot \cdot$ $(SCN)_2^{2-}$. The anation reaction may thus be developed using the model in Eq. (3-13), where K is the equilibrium constant for formation of the

$$Co(NH_3)_5OH_2^{3+} + X^- \overset{K}{\rightleftharpoons} Co(NH_3)_5OH_2^{3+} \cdots X^-$$

$$Co(NH_3)_5OH_2^{3+} \cdots X^- \overset{k}{\to} Co(NH_3)_5X^{2+} \cdots OH_2$$

(3-13)

first outer sphere complex and k is the rate constant for anion entry. The rate constants do not differ by more than a factor of 8, and most of the difference may be accounted for statistically. If there are eight sites in the outer coordination sphere, only one will be the appropriate position for replacement of the leaving water molecule. The chances are then 1 out of 8 that the X^- group will replace the leaving water; the other times, a water enters. Thus the *expected* anation rate for a monovalent anion is the water exchange rate multiplied by a statistical factor, $s = 0.13$. (If an anion (perhaps SO_4^{2-}) can replace two water molecules in the outer sphere, its chance of reaction should increase to 2 out of 8, and the s factor for multiplying the water exchange rate should be 0.25.) If these statistical corrections are applied it is seen that all five entering groups react at *very nearly* the same rate. Thus, the reaction is **I**, since the consequences of an intermediate cannot be realized, and $\mathbf{I_d}$ because the rate is insensitive to the nature of the entering group.

(The ion association constant used for chloride in this argument is controversial. But, a reinterpretation of its value would not seriously affect the argument. The reaction in the $[Co(NH_3)_5OH_2]^{3+} \cdots Cl^-$ outer-sphere complex would still fall below the water-exchange rate if the constant for formation of the aggregate were only about 1.0.)

3-11 EVIDENCE FOR D PROCESSES

The best documented example of a **D** process is reaction (3-14), studied

$$Co(CN)_5X^{3-} + H_2O \rightleftharpoons Co(CN)_5OH_2^{2-} + X^-$$

(3-14)

by Haim and Wilmarth.[40a] This system has the advantage that outer-sphere association constants should be very small, since the species involved carry like charges. Equation (3-4) may be rewritten for this system as Eq. (3-15), from which it follows that observed pseudo first-order rate con-

$$Co(CN)_5OH_2^{2-} \underset{k_{-1}}{\overset{k_1}{\rightleftharpoons}} Co(CN)_5^{2-} + H_2O$$

$$Co(CN)_5^{2-} + X^- \overset{k_2}{\to} Co(CN)_5X^{3-}$$

(3-15)

stants for anation (when the anion is present in excess) should conform to expression (3-16), according to the argument given in Section 3-2. At

$$k_{obs} = \frac{k_1[X^-]}{[X^-] + k_{-1}/k_2} \qquad (3\text{-}16)$$

40°C, ionic strength 1.0, and pH = 6.4, k_{-1}/k_2 was found to be 1.9 for $X^- = N_3^-$ and 2.95 for $X^- = SCN^-$; 5.15 for $X^- = I^-$ and 10 for $X^- = Br^-$. The value of k_1 was 1.6×10^{-3} sec^{-1}. k_1 represents the rate of generation of the five-coordinate intermediate from $Co(CN)_5OH_2^{2-}$ and should agree with the rate of water exchange in the absence of anions. Although difficulties arose in the separation steps of ^{18}O experiments, the rate of water exchange could be placed at the order of magnitude of 10^{-3} sec^{-1}.

Halpern and Palmer [40b] have obtained similar kinetic evidence for the intermediate $Co(NH_3)_4SO_3^+$ in reactions of $Co(NH_3)_4(SO_3)(OH)$ and $Co(NH_3)_5SO_3^+$ from the role of OH^-, NH_3, and CN^- in the rate laws. These workers point out that the competition experiments give an order of reactivity of nucleophiles toward the five-coordinate **D** intermediates as follows: toward $Co(CN)_5^{2-}$, $H_2O:NH_3:OH^- = 1:4:6 \times 10^4$; toward $Co(NH_3)_4SO_3^+$, $H_2O:NH_3:CN^-:OH^- = 1:1 \times 10^2:2 \times 10^3:1.7 \times 10^5$.

In some of the nonaqueous-solvent work, a method of detecting **D** processes has emerged that is not applicable to corresponding reactions in aqueous solutions. The chloride-independent part of the radiochloride-exchange reaction of *trans*-$Co(en)_2Cl_2^+$ in methanol must be either a **D** process or one in which the first step is entry of methanol into the first coordination sphere. The second alternative requires that methanol be sufficiently *labile* to account for the over-all rate of exchange. If replacement of methanol by chloride is too slow, this path is excluded. Tobe has recently prepared the complexes $Co(en)_2Cl(MeOH)^{2+}$ and claimed [48] that the anation reaction in methanol is too slow for the methanol-containing complex to function as an intermediate in the radiochloride exchange. Therefore, the chloride-independent path must be **D**. A similar argument indicates at least some contribution of a **D** path to the same reaction in dimethylsulfoxide. [48]

A technique for detecting labile intermediates that has been of considerable importance in organic chemistry is the Winstein special salt effect. [56, 57] In a solvent in which outer-sphere association is pronounced, dissociation of the leaving group may produce the intermediate of a **D** path associated with the leaving group and yielding no net reaction. If, however, there is an ion present in the medium which may form an outer-sphere complex but is inert as far as inner-sphere complex formation is concerned, it may equilibrate with the outer-sphere complex of the intermediate and *preserve* the intermediate for reaction with the solvent. A hypothetical example is given in Eq. (3-17), where S designates the

$$
\begin{array}{c}
RX \xrightarrow[\;k_{-1}\;]{\;k_1\;} R^+ \cdots X^- \\[2mm]
\nwarrow{\scriptstyle k_3} \quad \Big\Vert \; {\scriptstyle k_{-2}}\; ClO_4^- \\
RS^+ \quad S \\
\xleftarrow[\;k_4\;]{} (R^+ \cdots ClO_4^-)
\end{array}
\qquad (3\text{-}17)
$$

solvent. In this example, replacement of X^- with ClO_4^- in the outer sphere prevents the five-coordinate intermediate from recombining with X^- and allows it to react with S, increasing the observed solvolysis rate.

In organic reactions, it has proved possible to observe special salt effects only in the least polar media in which electrolytes could be dissolved. The special salt effect may be more common in reactions of complex ions with their larger charges and considerable tendency to association.[38, 58] It has not been demonstrated.

In conclusion, it may not be entirely foolhardy to venture some speculation about the factors leading to **D** as opposed to I_d substitutions. First, some ligands whose electronic effects stabilize the five-coordinate intermediate are probably required. This may mean either a good π-donor or a good π-acceptor group. Second, the less reactive the solvent the better *unless* it becomes so poor as not to solvate the intermediate effectively. Third, as Haim and Wilmarth observed, the complex with an over-all negative charge may be solvated in such a way that the solvent molecules are not properly oriented for entry. An I_d reaction might then require substantial reorganization of the outer sphere, in which case entry of a ligand from outside is almost equally probable.

3-12 ACID-CATALYZED PROCESSES

The "acid hydrolysis" reaction described above is normally pH-independent once the solution is sufficiently acid to make base hydrolysis negligible, but there are some examples of genuinely acid-catalyzed reactions. For example, hydrolysis of $Co(NH_3)_5F^{2+}$ is acid-dependent,[13] presumably because of the pre-equilibrium shown in Eq. (3-18). Proton-

$$
\begin{aligned}
Co(NH_3)_5F^{2+} + H_3O^+ &\rightleftharpoons Co(NH_3)_5FH^{3+} + H_2O \\
Co(NH_3)_5FH^{3+} + H_2O &\rightarrow Co(NH_3)_5OH_2^{3+} + HF
\end{aligned}
\qquad (3\text{-}18)
$$

ation of the leaving-group functions to increase its lability.   Similar behavior is found for systems such as $Co(NH_3)_5CO_3^+$, $Co(NH_3)_5ONO^{2+}$,
and $Co(en)_2F_2^+$.   In each case, it is quite plausible to assume that the
leaving group is being protonated.   This type of acid catalysis is related
to the catalysis of halide loss by Hg^{2+}, Ag^+, and Tl^+ mentioned above.

There is another form of acid catalysis possible for chelated compounds and that deserves mention, although it is easier to give an illus-
tration that is not a Co(III) complex.   The effect of acid on $Fe(bipy)_3^{2+}$
hydrolysis is thought to be the result of operation of mechanism (3-19).*

$$H_2O + Fe(bipy)_3^{2+} \rightleftharpoons Fe(bipy)_2(bipy-)OH_2^{2+}$$

$$H^+ + Fe(bipy)_2(bipy-)OH_2^{2+} \rightleftharpoons Fe(bipy)_2(bipyH)OH_2^{3+} \quad (3\text{-}19)$$

$$\rightarrow \text{hydrolysis}$$

In this case, protonation prevents the chelate group which is half dissociated from returning to the bidentate form and thereby encourages hydrolysis.   It is expected that at some acid concentration the half-disso-
ciated ligand would be $\sim$100 per cent protonated and that the rate would
reach a limit.   In the example, this limiting rate is observed above
$\sim$1.5 M acid.[59]

3-13   SUMMARY OF Co(III) SUBSTITUTION REACTIONS

The major mechanism of substitution at Co(III) centers in acid solution involves a dissociative activation process in which the complex must
accumulate most of the activation energy without significant bonding to
the entering group.   The main lines of evidence are the following.

1. The accessibility to kinetic study of only two reactions: acid
hydrolysis and its reverse, anation.

2. The systematic failure of all attempts to identify selective reagents
for attack at Co(III), even in nonaqueous solutions.

3. The emergence of a unified interpretation of leaving-group effects,
charge effects, steric effects, chelation effects, and even nonlabile ligand
effects on the basis of the hypothesis of dissociative activation.

The major mechanism of rapid base hydrolysis involves the *conjugate
base* of the complex in a reaction which is analogous to acid hydrolysis.
The main lines of evidence are the following:

1. The requirement of an acid proton for rapid base hydrolysis.

2. The separability of the hydroxide-dependent step from the product-
determining step.

* (bipy-) indicates that one end of bidentate ligand is dissociated.

Although it seems possible to generalize about the *energetics* of Co(III) substitutions, it emerges that similar *intimate* pathways may correspond to distinct *stoichiometric* pathways. Evidence exists for pathways both with and without a five-coordinate intermediate, D and I_d.

3-14 ACID HYDROLYSIS AND ANATION OF Cr(III) AND Rh(III) COMPLEXES

The Cr(III)-ammine complexes are more difficult to prepare than the corresponding Co(III) complexes. It is not yet possible to compare analogous Cr(III) systems with all the Co(III) data. The halopentammines do undergo aquation with the rate decreasing along the sequence $I^- > Br^- > Cl^- \gg NCS^-$.[3, 60] The rates are about 10 times the analogous $Co(NH_3)_5X^{2+}$ rates. The elegant studies of rate and stereochemistry in the acid hydrolysis reactions of *cis*- and *trans*-$Cr(en)_2Cl_2^+$ by Garner and his co-workers [61-63] suggest parallels to Co(III) in structural effects and stereochemistry. Surprisingly, the activation energies are almost identical to the analogous Co(III) values.

An especially striking demonstration that acid hydrolysis and its reverse are the only accessible reactions was provided by Jones et al.[64] in their study of anion-catalyzed hydrolysis of $Cr(NH_3)_5Br^{2+}$. They observed that divalent organic anions (for example, *o*-phthalate, maleate) catalyzed the loss of Br^-. The initial product was $Cr(NH_3)_5OH^{2+}$, corresponding to water entry. This, despite the fact that the anion slowly replaced the OH^- group to form the anionic complex at equilibrium. The catalytic effect of the anion was proportional to the outer-sphere association constant of the anion with $Co(NH_3)_6^{3+}$, and was, therefore, attributed to formation of an outer-sphere ion pair. *The group that is thermodynamically preferred is present in the outer-sphere during these reactions, but water still functions as the entering group.*

One way to understand this interesting result is in terms of an I_d mechanism. The outer-sphere complex probably forms with the anion on the opposite side of the complex from the negatively charged leaving group. Thus, when the bond to the leaving group is broken, the molecule in position to enter the vacancy is a second-sphere *water*.

There remains an interesting and extensive class of Cr(III) complexes whose analogs in Co(III) chemistry are unstable. They are the derivatives of $Cr(OH_2)_6^{3+}$. The kinetics are familiar. There is an acid hydrolysis reaction of $Cr(H_2O)_5X^{2+}$ which is first order over-all. The reactions have a term inverse in $[H^+]$ attributable to reaction of hydroxide with the complexes to form a conjugate base (for example, $Cr(OH_2)_5$-$(OH)^{2+}$). The conjugate bases react more rapidly than the acid forms, presumably as a result of the labilizing effect of hydroxide as a substituent.

The leaving-group effect in acid hydrolyses of $Cr(OH_2)_5X^{2+}$ yields the familiar decreasing rate sequence [65-67] $Br^- > Cl^- > NCS^-$. Rates of acid hydrolysis of cis- and trans-$Cr(OH_2)_4Cl_2^+$ are only about ten times faster than hydrolysis of $Cr(OH_2)_5Cl^{2+}$ and, in contrast to the ammine complexes, the trans isomer reacts a little faster than the cis.[68]

There have been important studies of the anation reactions of $Cr(OH_2)_6^{3+}$, one by Hamm and his collaborators, [69] and one by Postmus and King.[67] The rate of water exchange has also been measured by the ^{18}O technique.[70] Hamm et al. report anation of $Cr(OH_2)_6^{3+}$ by a series of anions of organic acids. The rates are independent of the anion concentration, probably because outer-sphere complexes have been formed at the high anion concentration. The rates are also pH dependent, suggesting once again the greater reactivity of the conjugate base. But, the most interesting result is that the anation rates are independent of the nature of the anion. Within experimental error, acetate, oxalate, malonate, lactate, citrate, tartrate, glycolate, and phthalate all enter at the same rate. This is some evidence for the lack of entering-group assistance in the anations and favors either an I_d or D mechanism. Postmus and King studied SCN^- entry, a slightly simpler system, since the anion is not so basic. At low thiocyanate, they found a second-order term, $k[complex][SCN^-]$, in the rate law with $k = 1.9 \times 10^{-6}$ M^{-1} sec^{-1} at 25°C. They also report that the formation constant of the outer-sphere complex between $Cr(OH_2)_6^{3+}$ and SCN^- is 7. Following the procedure used above, we may estimate the value of the pseudo-first order rate constant when the ratio of the outer-sphere ion-pair concentration to the concentration of unassociated $Cr(OH_2)_6^{3+}$ is 10. The rate constant would be $\sim 2.7 \times 10^{-6}$ sec^{-1}. The situation is unlike the $Co(NH_3)_5OH_2^{3+}$ situation in that the anation rate in the 1:1 outer-sphere complex is close to the water-exchange rate, instead of being substantially smaller. The factor s is only a little less than one. This could be interpreted as indication of a D path for this reaction. If the five-coordinate intermediate is formed, it need not simply react with the ligand in position (determined statistically); it may survive long enough to show significant preference for the outer-sphere thiocyanate over the outer-sphere water. The alternative of an I_d process slightly sensitive to the entering group would be less easily reconciled with Hamm's results. The five-coordinate intermediate hypothesis appears to be supported by Ardon's recent observation [71a] that Cl^- may replace I^- in $Cr(OH_2)_5I^{2+}$ directly, without intervention of $Cr(OH_2)_6^{3+}$, supplemented by the observation that added I^- retards the reaction. But, a careful ^{18}O tracer study of this system by Moore and co-workers [71b] has shown that iodide has a strong trans labilizing effect. The apparent "direct" replacement of I^- by Cl^- actually goes along the path $Cr(OH_2)_5I^{2+} \rightarrow$ $Cr(OH_2)_4(I)Cl^+ \rightarrow Cr(OH_2)_5Cl^{2+}$. The stoichiometric mechanism of each substitution remains uncertain.

Although they will not be reviewed here, mention should be made of the extensive studies of reactions of *tris*-oxalatochromate(III) ion and its derivatives.[72]

One important systematic study of the behavior of Rh(III)-ammine complexes has been published.[73] The results are extensive enough to permit comparison to Co(III) on several points. The most important is that acid hydrolysis and base hydrolysis are the dominant reactions. Evidence was presented to show that the nucleophiles Br^-, SCN^-, CN^-, SO_3^{2-}, $S_2O_3^{2-}$, N_3^-, OH^-, NO_2^-, I^-, Cl^-, thiourea, and NH_3 all attack *trans*-$Rh(en)_2Cl_2^+$ at the same rate. No nucleophile is superior to water; the mechanism is most probably I_d or **D**. This conclusion is supported by the observation of steric effects similar to, but smaller than, those reported for Co(III). The reduction in magnitude is expected for the larger Rh(III) ion. There is a chelate effect (also smaller) similar to that discussed above for Co(III) amines. Important differences between the Co(III) and Rh(III) systems emerge in that the replacement of an amine ligand by chloride does not lead to significant acceleration of acid hydrolysis, charge does not seem as important in Rh(III) complexes, and the stereochemical result of both acid and base hydrolysis of *trans*-$Rh(en)_2Cl_2^+$ is complete retention. If the stereochemical and accelerating effects of chloride are due to π donation which relieves electron repulsion by utilization of the orbital becoming empty in the transition state (as was argued explicitly in Section 3-7), we might expect smaller effects for second and third transition series metals. The interelectronic-repulsion integrals (from electronic spectra) are much smaller for the *ground-state complexes*.

The reactions of the Rh(III) ammines are at least two orders of magnitude slower than those of Co(III) ammines, and limited data [74] indicate that the reactions of the iridium complexes are even slower. The differences, however, are not nearly so large as the rate differences in Ni(II), Pd(II), and Pt(II) reactions.

3-15 Cr(III) AND RELATED BASE HYDROLYSIS REACTIONS

In comparison to Co(III) amines, *trans* π donors have smaller effects on acid hydrolysis reactions of Cr(III) [62, 63] and Rh(III) [73] ammines. This leads to the prediction that base hydrolysis will be a less prominent reaction, since the very rapid reaction of the conjugate base is attributed to the outstanding π-donor ability of the amide ligand. Predictions must, however, also take into account the equilibrium constant for transfer of a proton from an ammine ligand to hydroxide. Equation (3-9) pointed out that the observed second-order rate constant for base hydrolysis is the product of the equilibrium constant for proton transfer and the rate constant for hydrolysis of the conjugate base.

The difficulty that plagues analysis of Co(III) base hydrolysis rates also complicates the present discussion; the equilibrium constants are not available. But, rates of H-D exchange are available for several complexes. These probably do provide good estimates of relative acidity, because it is probable that recombination of the amide ligand with a proton is very fast and nearly independent of the metal. The exchange rate is controlled by the rate of transfer of a proton from the complex to OH^- and, if the reverse reaction is metal independent, the acidity constant will also be proportional to this rate. Table 3-5 contains the hydrogen-deuterium exchange rates for several $M(NH_3)_6^{3+}$ ions and the acidity constants of corresponding $M(NH_3)_5OH_2^{2+}$ ions. The acidity constants of the aquo complexes generally support the argument that exchange rates are proportional to acidity constants. Table 3-5, therefore, includes estimated relative K values for the ammine-proton loss based on the measured exchange rates.

Table 3-5 also includes three kinetic parameters for the complexes $Rh(NH_3)_5Cl^{2+}$, $Cr(NH_3)_5Cl^{2+}$, $Co(NH_3)_5Cl^{2+}$, and $Ru(NH_3)_5Cl^{2+}$; the

Table 3-5   *Acidity properties and hydrolysis rates of several metal-ammine complexes* [a]

Metal ion	Cr^{3+}	Co^{3+}	Rh^{3+}	Ru^{3+}
k H-D exchange 25°C of $M(NH_3)_6^{3+}$, M^{-1} sec^{-1}	2.6×10^6	1.6×10^6	2.1×10^5	6.0×10^8
pK_a of $M(NH_3)_5OH_2^{3+}$, 25°C	5.2	5.7	5.9	4.2
K_a of $M(NH_3)_5Cl^{2+}$ [b] relative to $Co(NH_3)_5Cl^{2+}$	1.6	1.0	0.13	3.7×10^2
k_{OH^-} of $M(NH_3)_5Cl^{2+}$, M^{-1} sec^{-1}, 25°C	1.65×10^{-3}	8.5×10^{-1}	2×10^{-3}	2.9
k_{H_2O} of $M(NH_3)_5Cl^{2+}$, sec^{-1}, 25°C	8.3×10^{-6}	1.7×10^{-6}	4.3×10^{-5}	3.3×10^{-4}
$k_{OH^-}/k_{H_2O}K_a$ [b] of $M(NH_3)_5Cl^{2+}$	1.2×10^2	5.0×10^5	3.6×10^2	4×10^1

[a] The data on which this table is based appeared in Table IV of the paper by J. A. Broomhead, F. Basolo, and R. G. Pearson [*Inorg. Chem.*, **3**, 826 (1964)]. Sources of the information are cited there.

[b] Estimated as described in the text.

rate of acid hydrolysis, the rate of base hydrolysis, and the relative rate of base to acid hydrolysis *corrected* for relative acidity. The final quantities test the *first* prediction, showing the effect of changing from an ammine to an amide ligand on the rate of a hydrolysis reaction. The effect decreases in the order Co(III) $\gg$ Rh(III) $\sim$ Cr(III) > Ru(III). Because of the higher acidity of the Ru(III) complex, its observed base hydrolysis rate is fast.

Earlier in the chapter, it was suggested that ligands which facilitate hydrolysis reactions by π donation anticorrelated to some extent with ligands of high nephelauxetic effect. It was suggested that the mechanism of assistance was delocalization of electrons into empty orbitals in the transition state to reduce interelectronic repulsions. This idea is consistent with the series Co(III) $\gg$ Rh(III) $\sim$ Cr(III) > Ru(III), since this would be reasonable version of the order of decreasing ground-state interelectronic repulsions. Along this series, more electron delocalization is expected in the ground-state octahedral complex, and therefore there is less advantage in producing the transition state with an empty orbital.

3-16 MECHANISMS EMPLOYED BY OTHER OCTAHEDRAL COMPLEXES

The review published by Taube [75] in 1952 set the terms of reference beginning the current period of active interest in ligand substitutions. At that point, most metal complexes could only be called *labile*. This was still true when the theory of substitution processes could be reviewed exhaustively, as it was in the important book of Basolo and Pearson [76] in 1958. In the years since, the situation has changed radically as a result of the introduction of methods for the study of reaction rates up to and including the diffusion-controlled limit. Some of the "slower" reactions of labile complexes have been measured by flow methods,[77] but the breakthrough is a result of application of the relaxation methods developed by Eigen and his collaborators [78] (especially the sound absorption and temperature-jump techniques), and use of nmr relaxation-time studies, especially those of Connick [79] and his co-workers.

Although the methods are not limited in principle and their applications are being rapidly extended, most of the studies to date concern the formation of complexes containing nonsolvent ligands from the aquometal ions [Eq. (3-20)] and the exchange of water molecules between the first

$$Ni(OH_2)_6^{2+} + SO_4^{2-} \rightarrow Ni(OH_2)_4SO_4 + 2H_2O \qquad (3\text{-}20)$$

coordination sphere and the bulk solvent (nmr method). The available information, then, is for *one* leaving group and a variety of entering groups.

Fortunately, the relaxation methods may permit distinguishing the process of outer-sphere complex formation from entry into the inner sphere in cases where the second step is significantly slower than diffusion control, so that the formation rates discussed are those for the first-order process of ligand entry from the second sphere into the first; thus, results for different ligands may be directly compared.

It has emerged that metal ions in aqueous solution fall into three well-defined categories [78]:

1. Very rapid ligand-dependent reactions are observed for complex formation by alkali metals (Li^+, Na^+, K^+, Rb^+, Cs^+) and the alkaline earth metals Ca^{2+}, Sr^{2+}, and Ba^{2+}. The rate constants are greater than 10^7 sec^{-1} with all ligands, and there is some variation in rate from ligand to ligand. Rate increase correlates with decrease in the heat of hydration of the metal ion.

2. A group of cations, including most of the divalent metals of the first transition series, Mg^{2+}, and some reactions of trivalent rare earth ions exhibit rate constants less than 10^7 sec^{-1} and very nearly independent of the nature of the entering ligand.

3. A few cations display still lower rates of ligand entry and water exchange which vary as the basicity of the entering group. Examples are Fe^{3+}, Al^{3+}, and Be^{2+}.

The reactions in the first category could only be studied with strongly complexing ligands such as EDTA, nitrilotriacetic acid, and adenosine triphosphate. It appears that water loss is sufficiently facile that ligand

Table 3-6   *Rates of complex formation and water exchange* [a]

Ligand	$\log k$, $M^{-1} sec^{-1}$ [b]		
	Ni^{2+}	Co^{2+}	Fe^{2+}
H_2O	4.4	6.0	6.5
SO_4^{2-}	4.2	5.3	6.0
o-phenanthroline	3.2	5.5	5.9
SCN^-		4.0	
glycylglycine	4.3	5.7	
$C_2O_4^{2-}$	4.9		

[a] Data from a tabulation by M. Eigen and R. C. Wilkins, "Mechanisms of Inorganic Reactions," Summer Symposium of the Division of Inorganic Chemistry of the American Chemical Society, Lawrence, Kansas, June 21–24, 1964.
[b] Except solvent exchange which is in sec^{-1}.

Table 3-7   *Reactions of ferric ion with anions at 25°C* [a, b]

Anion	k, $M^{-1} sec^{-1}$	$\Delta H\ddagger$, kcal mole^{-1}	$\Delta S\ddagger$, eu	k_1, sec^{-1}
F$^-$	1×10^4	23 ± 2.5	35 ± 9	
SO$_4^{2-}$	6.4×10^3	18 ± 2	19 ± 7	720
SCN$^-$	127	13 ± 1.4	-5 ± 5	
Cl$^-$	9.4	16 ± 2	2 ± 6	18 ± 2
Br$^-$	20			13 ± 8

[a] Rate law: $d(\text{FeSCN}^{2+})/dt = k_1[\text{Fe}^{3+}][\text{SCN}^-] + k_2[\text{Fe}^{3+}][\text{SCN}^-][\text{H}^+]^{-1}$.

[b] See J. F. Below, R. E. Connick, and C. P. Coppel, *J. Am. Chem. Soc.*, **80**, 2961 (1958); R. E. Connick and C. P. Coppel, *J. Am. Chem. Soc.*, **81**, 6389 (1959); and the critical review in E. F. Caldin, *Fast Reactions in Solution*, Wiley, New York, 1964, p. 49.

attack is the rate-determining step, but it is doubtful that conventional considerations of "nucleophilicity" of the attacking atom are relevant to discussion of the rates of ligand attack. Eigen suggests that the rate-limiting step in these processes is the replacement of several water molecules by the multidentate ligand.

The behavior in the second category is familiar. This category would include almost all the slow reactions discussed earlier in this chapter. The entering group is clearly not an important participant in the transition state, and the reactions are either I_d or **D**. Again, it seems reasonable to generalize about the dissociative character of the transition states but it is probably not possible to generalize concerning the question of an intermediate of reduced coordination number. One interesting feature does appear. Table 3-6 gives some data for several ligands reacting with the aquo-Co^{2+}, aquo-Fe^{2+}, and aquo-Ni^{2+} ions. In these cases, there is an analogy to the anation reactions of Co(NH$_3$)$_5$OH$_2^{3+}$. The water-exchange process is *faster* than all of the anations but one. (One must be cautious of the fact that the water-exchange rates come from an entirely different experimental method than the anation reaction rates.)

The third category includes slow reactions showing definitely higher rates with basic ligands. The transition-metal case is that of the hexaquoferric ion for which data are collected in Table 3-7. These data might be interpreted as indicative of a shift away from **d** reaction, but an alternative explanation has been offered.[78] The parallel of reactivity with basicity suggests that the effect of the ligand may be to act as a proton acceptor. In these reactions, the rate of hydrolysis is greater than the rate of water substitution, and pH effects show that the hydrolyzed species undergoes faster substitution. The reaction may proceed by transfer of a proton to the entering group in the outer sphere followed by loss of a water molecule from the inner sphere [Eq. (3-21)]. There is one serious diffi-

$$
\begin{aligned}
\text{Fe—OH}_2^{3+} \cdots \text{B}^- &\rightarrow \text{Fe—OH}^{2+} \cdots \text{BH} \\
\text{Fe—OH}^{2+} \cdots \text{BH} &\rightarrow \text{FeB}^{2+} \cdots \text{OH}_2
\end{aligned}
\tag{3-21}
$$

culty that this proposal must face. It appears that the "internal hydroly-sis" envisioned occurs for Al^{3+} and Fe^{3+} but not for Cr^{3+}, since the hexa-quochromic ion rates are not sensitive to ligand basicity. (For example, SO_4^{2-} entry occurs at the same rate as SCN^- entry.) In the Cr^{3+} case the conditions of slow water exchange and fast hydrolysis are met and, al-though the Cr^{3+} ion is a weaker acid than the Fe^{3+} ion, it is a stronger acid than the Al^{3+} ion. Perhaps a reconciliation can be achieved if the Cr^{3+} ion reactions are D, whereas the Al^{3+} and Fe^{3+} reactions are I_d. But, there is some reason to believe that Fe(III) may mark a shift to the I_a mechanism. It is noteworthy that the ethylenediaminetetraacetic acid complex of Fe(III) has a coordination number of seven.[80] (That the strained ring requires distortion from an octahedron in the highly chelated complex may have something to do with the occurrence of the seven coordination.)

It may be appropriate, here, to note that some significant evidence does exist for a substitution in one Fe(II) system: the *tris-(o-*phenanthro-line)iron(II) ion. Margerum and Morgenthaler [81] demonstrated that decomposition of this complex is accelerated by CN^-, OH^-, and N_3^- ions (effectiveness decreasing in that order). Richards and co-workers [82] have shown that the acid-catalyzed (see Section 3-12) decomposition of this Fe(II) complex slows down in nearly pure H_2SO_4, whereas the decom-position of the analogous Ni(II) complex does not. They suggest that the Fe(II) complex requires water attack (a), whereas the Ni(II) does not.

REFERENCES

1. F. Basolo, B. D. Stone, and R. G. Pearson, *J. Am. Chem. Soc.*, **76,** 3079 (1954).
2. R. G. Pearson and J. W. Moore, *Inorg. Chem.*, **3,** 1334 (1964).
3. A. W. Adamson and R. G. Wilkins, *J. Am. Chem. Soc.*, **76,** 3379 (1954).
4. G. W. Ettle and C. H. Johnson, *J. Chem. Soc.*, **1940,** 1490.
5. C. H. Langford and M. P. Johnson, *J. Am. Chem. Soc.*, **86,** 229 (1964).
6. M. G. Church, E. D. Hughes, C. K. Ingold, and N. A. Taher, *J. Chem. Soc.*, **1940,** 971.
7. J. O. Edwards and R. G. Pearson, *J. Am. Chem. Soc.*, **84,** 16 (1962).
8. R. G. Pearson, C. R. Boston, and F. Basolo, *J. Am. Chem. Soc.*, **75,** 3089 (1953).
9. J. E. Leffler and E. Grunwald, *Rates and Equilibria of Organic Reactions*, Wiley, New York, 1963, p. 156ff.

10. C. H. Langford, *Inorg. Chem.*, **4**, 265 (1965).
11. A. Haim and H. Taube, *Inorg. Chem.*, **2**, 1199 (1963).
12. R. G. Yalman, *Inorg. Chem.*, **1**, 16 (1962).
13. S. C. Chan, *J. Chem. Soc.*, **1964**, 2375.
14. K. B. Yatsimirskii and L. Pankova, *Zh. Obshch. Khim.*, **19**, 611 (1949); K. B. Yatsimirskii, *Zh. Obshch. Khim.*, **20**, 1408 (1950).
15. See, for example, the table in C. K. Jørgensen, *Absorption Spectra and Chemical Bonding in Complexes*, Addison-Wesley, Reading, Mass., 1962. Chap. 7.
16. R. A. D. Wentworth and T. S. Piper, *Inorg. Chem.*, **4**, 709 (1965).
17. H. B. Gray, *Electrons and Chemical Bonding*, Benjamin, New York, 1964, p. 198.
18. M. E. Baldwin, S. C. Chan, and M. L. Tobe, *J. Chem. Soc.*, **1961**, 4637.
19. R. G. Pearson, C. R. Boston, and F. Basolo, *J. Phys. Chem.*, **59**, 304 (1955).
20. J. N. Bronsted, *Z. Phys. Chem.*, **122**, 383 (1926).
21. M. L. Tobe, *J. Chem. Soc.*, **1959**, 3776.
22. C. K. Ingold, R. S. Nyholm, and M. L. Tobe, *Nature*, **187**, 477 (1960).
23. A. W. Adamson and F. Basolo, *Acta Chem. Scand.*, **9**, 1261 (1955).
24. F. Basolo, W. R. Matoush, and R. G. Pearson, *J. Am. Chem. Soc.*, **78**, 4883 (1956).
25. C. H. Langford and M. L. Tobe, *J. Chem. Soc.*, **1963**, 506.
26. R. G. Pearson, N. C. Stellwagen, and F. Basolo, *J. Am. Chem. Soc.*, **82**, 1077 (1960).
27. M. L. Tobe, *Sci. Progr. (London)*, **48**, 483 (1960).
28. F. J. Garrick, *Nature*, **139**, 507 (1937).
29. F. Basolo and R. G. Pearson, *Mechanisms of Inorganic Reactions*, Wiley, New York, 1958, Chap. 3.
30. F. Basolo and R. G. Pearson, *Advan. Inorg. Chem. Radiochem.*, **3**, 1 (1961).
31. R. G. Pearson, H. H. Schmidtke, and F. Basolo, *J. Am. Chem. Soc.*, **82**, 4434 (1960).
32. M. Green and H. Taube, *Inorg. Chem.*, **2**, 948 (1963).
33. J. W. Palmer and F. Basolo, *J. Inorg. Nucl. Chem.*, **15**, 279 (1960).
34. S. C. Chan and M. L. Tobe, *J. Chem. Soc.*, **1963**, 514.
35. S. Asperger and C. K. Ingold, *J. Chem. Soc.*, **1956**, 2862.
36. C. H. Langford, *Inorg. Chem.*, **3**, 228 (1964).
37. C. H. Langford and P. O. Langford, *Inorg. Chem.*, **2**, 300 (1963).
38. M. N. Hughes and M. L. Tobe, *J. Chem. Soc.*, **1965**, 1204.
39. Ref. 15, Chaps. 8 and 5.
40a. A. Haim and W. K. Wilmarth, *Inorg. Chem.*, **1**, 573 (1962); **1**, 583 (1962).
40b. J. Halpern and R. A. Palmer, private communication, 1965.
41. H. B. Gray, E. Billig, A. Wojcicki, and M. Farona, *Can. J. Chem.*, **41**, 1281 (1963).
42. D. D. Brown, C. K. Ingold, and R. S. Nyholm, *J. Chem. Soc.*, **1953**, 2673.
43. R. G. Pearson and F. Basolo, *J. Am. Chem. Soc.*, **78**, 4878 (1956).
44. C. K. Ingold, R. S. Nyholm, and M. L. Tobe, *Nature*, **194**, 344 (1962).
45. D. A. Buckingham, private communication, 1965.
45a. R. G. Pearson and F. Basolo, *Inorg. Chem.*, **4**, 1522 (1965).
46. D. F. Martin and M. L. Tobe, *J. Chem. Soc.*, **1961**, 4637.
47. A. M. Sargeson, *Australian J. Chem.*, **16**, 352 (1963).

48. M. L. Tobe, in *Mechanisms of Inorganic Reactions*, Summer Symposium of the Division of Inorganic Chemistry, American Chemical Society, Lawrence, Kansas, June 21–24, 1964.
49. F. A. Posey and H. Taube, *J. Am. Chem. Soc.*, **79**, 255 (1957).
50. A. M. Sargeson, *Australian J. Chem.*, **17**, 385 (1964).
51. D. Loeliger and H. Taube, *Inorg. Chem.*, **4**, 1032 (1965).
52. H. R. Hunt and H. Taube, *J. Am. Chem. Soc.*, **80**, 2642 (1958).
53. H. Taube and F. A. Posey, *J. Am. Chem. Soc.*, **75**, 1463 (1953).
54. W. Schmidt and H. Taube, *Inorg. Chem.*, **2**, 698 (1963).
55. C. H. Langford and P. O. Langford, to be published.
56. S. Winstein et al., *Chem. & Ind. (London)*, **1954**, 664.
57. S. Winstein and G. C. Robinson, *J. Am. Chem. Soc.*, **80**, 169 (1958); S. Winstein and A. H. Fainberg, *J. Am. Chem. Soc.*, **80**, 459 (1958); S. Winstein, P. E. Klinedeinst, and G. C. Robinson, *J. Am. Chem. Soc.*, **83**, 885 (1961).
58. M. L. Tobe and D. W. Watts, *J. Chem. Soc.*, **1962**, 4614.
59. J. H. Baxendale and P. George, *Trans. Faraday Soc.*, **46**, 736 (1950).
60. M. A. Levine, T. P. Jones, W. E. Harris, and W. J. Wallace, *J. Am. Chem. Soc.*, **83**, 2453 (1961).
61. C. S. Garner and D. J. MacDonald, in *Advances in Chemistry of Coordination Compounds* (S. Kirshner, ed.), Macmillan, New York, 1961, p. 266.
62. D. J. MacDonald and C. S. Garner, *Inorg. Chem.*, **1**, 20 (1962).
63. D. C. Olson and C. S. Garner, *Inorg. Chem.*, **2**, 558 (1963).
64. T. P. Jones, W. E. Harris, and W. J. Wallace, *Can. J. Chem.*, **39**, 2371 (1959).
65. F. A. Guthrie and E. L. King, *Inorg. Chem.*, **3**, 916 (1964).
66. R. J. Baltisberger and E. L. King, *J. Am. Chem. Soc.*, **86**, 795 (1964).
67. C. Postmus and E. L. King, *J. Phys. Chem.*, **59**, 1217 (1955).
68. H. B. Johnson and W. L. Reynolds, *Inorg. Chem.*, **2**, 468 (1963).
69. R. E. Hamm, R. L. Johnson, R. H. Perkins, and R. E. Davis, *J. Am. Chem. Soc.*, **80**, 4469 (1958).
70. J. P. Hunt and R. H. Plane, *J. Am. Chem. Soc.*, **76**, 5960 (1954).
71a. M. Ardon, *Proc. Chem. Soc.*, **1964**, 333; *Inorg. Chem.*, **4**, 372 (1965).
71b. P. Moore, F. Basolo, and R. G. Pearson, to be published.
72. See, for example, K. V. Krishnamerty and G. M. Harris, *J. Phys. Chem.*, **64**, 346 (1960); R. E. Harris and R. H. Perkins, *J. Am. Chem. Soc.*, **77**, 2083 (1955); F. D. Graziano and G. S. Harris, *J. Phys. Chem.*, **63**, 330 (1959); E. Bushra and C. H. Johnson, *J. Chem. Soc.*, **1939**, 1937; C. H. Johnson, *Trans. Faraday Soc.*, **31**, 1612 (1935); G. K. Schweitzer and J. L. Rose, Jr., *J. Phys. Chem.*, **56**, 428 (1952); and G. L. Welch and R. E. Hamm, *Inorg. Chem.*, **2**, 295 (1963).
73. S. A. Johnson, F. Basolo, and R. G. Pearson, *J. Am. Chem. Soc.*, **85**, 1741 (1963).
74. A. B. Lamb and L. F. Fairhall, *J. Am. Chem. Soc.*, **45**, 378 (1923).
75. H. Taube, *Chem. Revs.*, **50**, 69 (1952).
76. Ref. 29, Chaps. 1 and 2.
77. D. S. Popplewell and R. G. Wilkins, *J. Chem. Soc.*, **1955**, 4098; A. K. S. Ahmed and R. G. Wilkins, *J. Chem. Soc.*, **1959**, 3700.
78. M. Eigen, *Pure Appl. Chem.*, **6**, 97 (1963), reprinted in *Coordination Chemistry: Seventh International Conference*, Butterworths (for I.U.P.A.C.), London, 1963, p. 97.

79. T. J. Swift and R. E. Connick, *J. Chem. Phys.*, **37,** 307 (1962).
80. J. L. Hoard, M. Lind, and J. U. Silverton, *J. Am. Chem. Soc.*, **83,** 2770 (1961).
81. D. W. Margerum and L. P. Morgenthaler, in *Advances in the Chemistry of the Coordination Compounds* (S. Kirshner, ed.), Macmillan, New York, 1961, p. 481.
82. A. F. Richards, J. F. Ridd, and M. L. Tobe, *Chem. & Ind. (London)*, **43,** 1726 (1963).

Glossary of Abbreviations for Ligands and Other Groups

Abbreviation	*Name*	*Formula or structure*
AcO⁻	acetate	$CH_3C{<}^{O}_{O^-}$
acac	acetylacetonate	
4-ampy	4-amylpyridine	$CH_3CH_2CH_2CH_2CH_2-$
bipy	2,2'-bipyridyl	

Abbreviation	*Name*	*Formula or structure*
s-Bu	*s*-butyl	CH_3—CH_2—$\overset{\displaystyle H}{\underset{\displaystyle CH_3}{C}}$—
d,l-bn	*d,l*-butylenediamine	CH_3—$\overset{\displaystyle NH_2}{C}$—H H—$\overset{}{\underset{\displaystyle NH_2}{C}}$—$CH_3$
meso-bn	*meso*-butylenediamine	CH_3—$\overset{\displaystyle NH_2}{C}$—H CH_3—$\underset{\displaystyle NH_2}{C}$—H
diars	*o*-phenylenebis(dimethyl-arsine)	
dien	diethylenetriamine	NH_2 CH_2 CH_2 H—N CH_2 CH_2 NH_2

Abbreviation	*Name*	*Formula or structure*
DMF	dimethylformamide	$H-C{<}^{O}_{N(CH_3)_2}$
DMSO	dimethylsulfoxide	$(CH_3)_2SO$
EDTA	ethylenediaminetetra-acetic acid	structure of EDTA
en	ethylenediamine	$NH_2-CH_2-CH_2-NH_2$ (drawn vertically)
Et	ethyl	CH_3-CH_2-
Et$_4$dien	1,1,7,7-tetraethyl-diethylenetriamine	structure of tetraethyldiethylenetriamine
Me	methyl	CH_3-

Abbreviation	Name	Formula or structure
MeEt$_4$dien	1,1,7,7-tetraethyl-4-methyldiethylene-triamine	
o-phen	1,10-phenanthroline	
α-pic	α-picoline	
pip	piperidine	

Abbreviation	*Name*	*Formula or structure*
pn	propylenediamine	$CH_3-\underset{\displaystyle NH_2}{\overset{\displaystyle \overset{NH_2}{\underset{\displaystyle }{CH_2}}}{C}}-H$
py	pyridine	
tetrameen	2,2,3,3-tetramethyl- ethylenediamine	$CH_3-\underset{CH_3}{\overset{NH_2}{C}}-CH_3$ $CH_3-\underset{NH_2}{C}-CH_3$

Index

LIGAND SUBSTITUTION PROCESSES

COOPER H. LANGFORD

Amherst College

HARRY B. GRAY

Columbia University

A modern, concise, and critical account of inorganic substitution mechanisms is presented in this introduction to the fundamentals of chemical dynamics. The book is directed to research workers as well as to senior and graduate students taking courses in physical inorganic chemistry, advanced inorganic chemistry, and reaction kinetics and mechanisms. The authors formulate an approach to ligand substitution reactions which is closely adapted to recently discovered special features of these processes. There is extensive use of molecular orbital theory for discussion of electronic effects on reaction rates and an up-to-date review of planar and octahedral substitution reactions.

A primary advantage of this book is that, as an introductory text, it critically treats the two most important geometries as *examples* and does not concern itself with everything that has been written. Summaries at the end of each chapter provide an evaluation of the material covered.

COOPER H. LANGFORD, Associate Professor of Chemistry at Amherst College, received his A.B. from Harvard University (1956) and his Ph.D. from Northwestern University (1960). During 1959–1960 he attended University College, London, as a National Science Foundation Postdoctoral Fellow and, in 1964, was a visiting staff member of the Department of Chemistry at Columbia University.

Among Dr. Langford's main research interests are ligand substitution reactions of cobalt (III) complexes, and fast reaction and solvation studies by NMR techniques. He is a member of the American Chemical Society, Sigma Xi, and a Fellow of the Chemical Society (London).

HARRY B. GRAY received the B.S. degree from Western Kentucky College in 1957 and the Ph.D. in 1960 from Northwestern University, where his research in inorganic chemistry was carried out under the direction of Professors Ralph Pearson and Fred Basolo.

Dr. Gray was a National Science Foundation Fellow at the University of Copenhagen during 1960–1961, where he was associated with Professor Carl J. Ballhausen. In 1961 he joined the chemistry staff at Columbia University, where he is now Professor.

He has published more than forty papers in the area of theoretical inorganic chemistry and is an Alfred P. Sloan Research Fellow for 1964–1966. His research interests include inorganic reaction mechanisms and the interpretation of spectral and magnetic properties of transition metal complexes using molecular orbital theory.